This book is dedicated to
Shirley Simmons
who taught me the recipe of life.

You are holding in your hands the cookbook that caused me to have a cuisine breakdown. It all started out so innocently. I wanted to write the best cookbook . . . the very best cookbook . . . Not a bunch of recipes that rambled on for hundreds of pages with a picture here and a picture there. I wanted mine to be different. I wanted to make complete meals . . . balanced meals . . . really creative breakfasts, lunches and dinners that were easy to fix . . . not real expensive to make. . . low in fat and that tasted rich and wonderful. Well, if you have ever tried to create a recipe with those high standards . . . you know it isn't easy . . . and it wasn't.

Every morning at 7:00 a.m. a room full of dieticians, home economists, chefs and yours truly, sat around and discussed the sacred "3 meals a day" that have been handed down to us by our culinary foremothers. (You try getting up one morning as the sun is rising and have a discussion about Red Snapper in a spicy bell pepper sauce!)

On large blackboards we inscribed all our most favorite dishes and began pulling them apart, taking out the fat . . . and cream. Brainstorming what to put in, in its place. By 11:00 a.m. we took to the kitchen to test out our ideas. The next five hours were spent blending, chopping, slicing, cutting and shredding every edible known on planet Earth. (It looked like a food processor convention.)

Calories were counted . . . oil and margarine were measured carefully . . . salt was eliminated or reduced. We added . . . we subtracted . . . we tested . . . we threw out . . . we remade . . . we collapsed!

At about 2:00 p.m., just as my kitchen looked like we just catered a dinner for one thousand Tupperware salesmen, a van full of people pulled up looking very hungry. Yes, each day we had actual human beings come and taste recipes and comment on flavor—texture—color—and appearance. Our food tasters came from all walks of life. Of course, there were mothers who were in charge of making many meals, for many people many times; we had grandmothers who had been cooking for half a century; bachelors; food writers; and critics. Once we had a nun come to taste a Stuffed Heavenly Omelet.

At 8:00 p.m. the kitchen closed, the apron came off, sporting some very attractive ketchup, strawberry and stroganoff blobs and a few meals passed the industrial strength tests to get accepted in the cookbook.

You would think after a day like that, I would fall into a deep-dish-sleep, but no such luck. I dreamt about food: I was beating egg whites in a football helmet, roasting cornish hen at the White House and cutting radishes to look like Corvettes. I'd wake up in a cold sweat, turn on TV only to be haunted by miniature hamburgers dancing on rooftops. Before you know it, 7:00 a.m. would roll around and it would start all over again.

I can proudly say, as I sit here in the Sanitarium, that this Deal-A-Meal Cookbook is a gem. This cookbook is filled with tasty meals you will be proud to serve. As McDonald's says, "We did it all for you", and we did.

We have figured out the right portions and the perfect presentations. We have given you a beautiful color picture of each and every meal. If you are on Deal-a-Meal or any other exchange weight loss program, we will show you which cards and how many you will use for each meal.

I believe this cookbook will become your best friend and will help motivate that little chef inside of you.

As soon as they let me out of here I'll be tackling The Deal-A-Meal Microwave Cookbook.

Until then, keep cooking slim.

Love,

Richard Simmons

I've always enjoyed cooking and eating. My hobby was trying new recipes. I gained over 100 pounds in the first year of my marriage. After realizing that this body is the only one I have and that weighing over 300 pounds was killing me, I made a commitment to change my life. I put <u>me</u> first, for the first time in 5 years and I am now 100 pounds lighter and embarking on a new life. I still love to cook, but now I modify the recipes to fit the Deal-A-Meal program. I can eat pasta, casseroles, pizza, pastry, all without getting fat. Be creative and success can be yours too.

Bonita Mozzor

Deal-A-Meal is a weight loss program that I have taught at my Beverly Hills workout salon for years to help my students lose their unwanted pounds.

Since its humble beginnings it has become the fastest-growing weight loss program in America! It has helped tens of thousands of people just like you and me lose and keep off from as little as a few pounds to as much as a few hundred pounds.

Deal-A-Meal was designed with everyone in mind.

* Deal-A-Meal is for adults and children.
* Deal-A-Meal teaches weight loss and weight loss maintenance.
* Deal-A-Meal is the first program that actually tells you what to eat and how much to eat.
* Deal-A-Meal shows you meal combinations and explains the food groups and calories.
* Deal-A-Meal lets you eat just about anything, planning your menus around the foods you like.
* With Deal-A-Meal you will learn to eat other foods besides FAT!
* Deal-A-Meal budgets the food you take in each day.
* With Deal-A-Meal you will no longer be living at the mercy of your appetite.
* And with Deal-A-Meal, you'll look and feel the way you've wanted to for years.

The honest-to-goodness truth is that Deal-A-Meal really does work!

HOW TO PLAY DEAL-A-MEAL

If you have ever played cards before, you will feel right at home with Deal-A-Meal because Deal-A-Meal is made up of a deck of playing cards and a wallet to keep them in.. You play by dealing yourself breakfast, lunch, dinner and even snacks. You then use these cards as guides when buying your food and planning your meals.

The Deal-A-Meal cards represent the food groups your body requires on a daily basis. Deal-A-Meal shows you the proper portions you need to lose weight and still be healthy.

If you already own a Deal-A-Meal you'll find that your Deal-A-Meal cards are broken into 3 categories. (If you do not have a Deal-A-Meal kit turn to page 22 to see how to get one).

1. Food Cards

These cards break the food groups into eight colors of playing cards:

- Red for Meat
- Brown for Bread, Grain, Pasta
- White for Dairy Products
- Green for Vegetables
- Pink for Fruits
- Yellow for Fats
- Purple for Freebies
- Jokers for Special Treats

2. Menu Cards

These cards give meal suggestions for breakfast, lunch, dinner and snacks.

3. Combination Cards

These cards tell you what food cards are included in more complex, ready-made meals such as french fries or hamburgers .

On the opposite page is a height-weight chart that is also included with each Deal-A-Meal kit. I am not a chart person, but this one will tell you approximately what your ideal weight should be. If the chart says you should weigh 135 pounds and you weigh 180, then you need to lose 45 pounds.

Once the amount of weight you want to lose has been determined, you then look up what your daily caloric intake should be to achieve your weight goal. This information is shown on the Daily Caloric Level Chart shown here.

Daily Caloric Level Chart

	Calories	
	Women	**Men**
FIRST WEEK ONLY	1,000	1,000
After FIRST WEEK		
Need to lose less than 40 lbs.	1,200	1,400
Need to lose more than 40 lbs.	1,400	1,600

MEN

Height Feet	Inches	Small Frame	Medium Frame	Large Frame
5	2	128-134	131-141	138-150
5	3	130-136	133-143	140-153
5	4	132-138	135-145	142-156
5	5	134-140	137-148	144-160
5	6	136-142	139-151	146-164
5	7	138-145	142-154	149-168
5	8	140-148	145-157	152-172
5	9	142-151	148-160	155-176
5	10	144-154	151-163	158-180
5	11	146-157	154-166	161-184
6	0	149-160	157-170	164-188
6	1	152-164	160-174	168-192
6	2	156-168	164-178	172-197
6	3	158-172	167-182	176-202
6	4	162-176	171-187	181-207

WOMEN

Height Feet	Inches	Small Frame	Medium Frame	Large Frame
4	10	102-111	109-121	113-131
4	11	103-113	111-125	120-134
5	0	104-115	113-126	122-137
5	1	106-118	115-129	125-140
5	2	108-121	118-132	128-143
5	3	111-124	121-135	131-147
5	4	114-127	124-138	134-151
5	5	117-130	127-141	137-155
5	6	120-133	130-144	140-159
5	7	123-136	133-147	143-163
5	8	126-139	136-150	146-167
5	9	129-142	139-153	149-170
5	10	132-145	142-156	152-173
5	11	135-148	145-159	155-176
6	0	138-151	148-162	158-179

*Weights at ages 25-59 based on lowest mortality.

Weight in pounds according to frame (in indoor clothing weighing 5 pounds for men and 3 pounds for women; shoes with 1-inch heels).

(Reproduced courtesy of Metropolitan Life Insurance Company, 1984.)

There are many diets that restrict you to 700 and even 500 calories per day. These types of programs should be monitored by a doctor. Therefore everyone who begins Deal-A-Meal begins it safe. That means that everyone starts Deal-A-Meal at 1000 calories the first week. You then continue on a program that matches the weight you want to lose. Once you know what your daily caloric level is you can then find out how many food cards you're allowed to play with for the day. (This is done with the Card Limit Chart that is shown here).

1,000
If your Daily Caloric Level is 1,000 calories, you may use:

RED Meat	BROWN Bread	WHITE Dairy	GREEN Vege	PINK Fruit	YELLOW Fats	PURPLE Freebies	JOKER
■■	■■	□	■■	■■	□□	No	■
■■	■■	□	■	■	□□	Limit	■

1,200
If your Daily Caloric Level is 1,200 calories, you may use:

RED Meat	BROWN Bread	WHITE Dairy	GREEN Vege	PINK Fruit	YELLOW Fats	PURPLE Freebies	JOKER
■■■	■■■	□	■■	■■	□□	No	■
■■	■■	□	■■	■■	□□	Limit	■

1,400
If your Daily Caloric Level is 1,400 calories, you may use:

RED Meat	BROWN Bread	WHITE Dairy	GREEN Vege	PINK Fruit	YELLOW Fats	PURPLE Freebies	JOKER
■■■	■■■	□	■■	■■	□□□	No	■
■■■	■■■	□	■■	■■	□□	Limit	■

1,600
If your Daily Caloric Level is 1,600 calories, you may use:

RED Meat	BROWN Bread	WHITE Dairy	GREEN Vege	PINK Fruit	YELLOW Fats	PURPLE Freebies	JOKER
■■■	■■■■	□	■■■	■■■	□□□	No	■
■■■	■■■	□	■■	■■	□□	Limit	■

Let's say it's your first week on Deal-A-Meal and you must stay at 1,000 calories a day. The Card Limit Chart tells you that you are allowed the following amount of cards:

4 - Meat (red)	3 - Fruit (pink)
4 - Bread (brown)	4 - Fats (yellow)
2 - Dairy (white)	2 - Jokers
3 - Vege (green)	No limit - Freebies

On the back of the cards there is a list of the foods each card will "buy" you. These are the foods you can eat, in the exact portion you need to meet your weight loss goal.

Each Deal-A-Meal kit comes with a wallet that is used with your cards. The right side of the wallet has slots for Breakfast, Lunch, Dinner, and Snacks. The left side has slots that are used to hold the cards you are playing with for the day. Whenever you eat, you "buy" your food by moving the appropriate card from the left side of the wallet to the Breakfast, Lunch, Dinner, or Snack slot on the right. If you eat more than the cards you have been allotted, you will automatically know that you have gained weight that day.
(See illustration below).

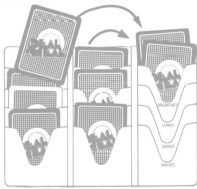

For example, let's say that for breakfast you decide that you would like to have a bran muffin, a glass of skim milk and a cup of black coffee. The bran muffin costs you 1 Bread Card, 1 Fat Card (for the shortening or margarine in the muffin) and 1 Fruit Card (for the raisins or other fruit in the muffin). The skim milk costs you 1 Dairy Card and your coffee is 1 Freebie card. All for a total of 280 calories. Now you pull out those cards — 1 Bread, 1 Fat, 1 Fruit, 1 Dairy, and 1 Freebie — and slide them from the slots on the left of your wallet into the Breakfast slots on the right.

You do this same process when you eat the rest of your meals and snacks. When you're out of cards on the left you're finished eating for the day. Finally you can watch your calories without counting them!

- The most healthy and permanent weight loss is gradual.
- Don't worry about ups and downs of a pound or two. Just make sure that there is an overall downward trend.
- Don't skip meals or concentrate all your eating into one big meal.
- Start with measuring cups and spoons, and a food scale if possible. Learn to "eyeball" correct portion size as soon as you can.
- Save a fruit, bread or dairy choice as a snack instead of as part of a meal.
- Eat your full allotment from all food cards every day. Starving is the quickest way to lose your health, not your weight.

MAINTENANCE - KEEPING THE NEW BEAUTIFUL YOU

So now you've lost your weight. 95% of all people on a diet gain their weight back... and that's why Deal-A-Meal has a maintenance program. So remember:

1. Be realistic about your goal weight.
2. Go below your goal weight by 2 or 3 pounds. This will give you some flexibility.
3. If you can't cut back on the calories, increase your exercise.
4. Balance your exercise with your eating plan, in order to maintain your weight.
5. Measure your weight and take body measurements. These two things are good indicators of how you're doing.
6. Don't skip meals. Make it a point to eat at least three balanced meals a day.

If your weight starts to creep up, you need to get right back onto your original Deal-A-Meal program.

Now you've got to take some time and prepare your world and lifestyle for your Deal-A-Meal program.

DEAL-A-MEAL YOUR KITCHEN

- Clean out that kitchen cupboard where you keep all those special treats for company.
- Use your cookie jar as a flower pot and sell your candy dishes at your next garage sale.
- Get a food scale. Begin measuring out precise portions.
- Put away TV trays. The only place you're eating from now on is at the dining room or kitchen table.

DEAL-A-MEAL YOUR BATHROOM

- Get a good bathroom scale. Start using it every day at the same time of the day. If you're the kind of person who can't get on a scale every day, at least do it once a week.
- Get a full-length mirror for positive motivation.
- Get a tape measure. Sometimes it's good to know you're losing inches even if you're not losing weight.

Go through your closets. Go through your car. Go through the garage. Make sure the wrong kinds of food are not in your house!

DEAL-A-MEAL YOUR FAMILY AND FRIENDS

- Introduce your family and friends to the Deal-A-Meal program.
- Sit down with your kids, your spouse, your parents, your roommate. Let them know and understand what you're doing.

DEAL-A-MEAL AND YOUR SHOPPING LIST

- Use the menu cards to plan your meals and your shopping list for the entire week.
- Always shop with a list and stick to it!
- Never shop when you're hungry!
- Don't take friends shopping with you. Go by yourself.
- Try to shop before the sun goes down. The longer the day gets, the weaker the willpower gets.

1. There are no <u>half</u> cards. Even if a card is not fully utilized in a menu, the whole card must be counted.

2. Deal-A-Meal your kitchen by investing in non-stick pans and small baking pans, casseroles, and small storage containers. Get rid of all the ingredients you won't need now that you're following the Deal-A-Meal plan.

3. When small amounts of wine or beer are used in cooking, the alcohol burns off and does not need to be counted as a "fat" card.

4. Freebie Salad - This is any salad that utilizes unlimited vegetables on the purple Freebie Deal-A-Meal card, such as lettuce, spinach, cucumbers, watercress and endive.

5. All calorie counts are per serving.

6. Each recipe has been carefully planned to fit exactly with it's specific menu. So for the sake of accuracy, don't switch recipes from menu to menu.

7. All the card counting has been done for you within each menu. You are not at liberty to add or subtract ingredients.

8. Go for variety, don't get stuck in a rut with the same menus. Try them all.

9. Get a set of measuring cups and measuring spoons and a small scale and use them accurately for best results, especially when baking.

10. Be honest with yourself regarding portion sizes. The results depend entirely on your efforts. Good luck.

It's easy to eat out and still play "Deal-A-Meal".

HERE'S HOW:

1. Always take your cards with you and plan ahead of time exactly how many cards you will use for a given meal.

2. Ask for what you want even if it isn't on the menu. Be specific. Say how you want things prepared. Such as:
   - without butter
   - dressing on the side
   - no sauce
   - broiled, plain
   - steamed

3. Keep some emergency supplies with you such as herb tea bags and individually packed servings of lo-cal dressing.

4. Be vigilant about portion sizes.

CREATE BREAKFAST MENUS FROM SOME OF THESE SUGGESTIONS:

1. Fresh fruit or juice.

2. One egg, scrambled without butter or poached.

3. Whole wheat toast, half English muffin or bagel, with butter or cream cheese on the side

4. Oatmeal or unfrosted cereal.

5. One scoop cottage cheese.

6. Always ask if low-fat or non-fat milk is available. If not, count appropriate number of "fat" cards.

CREATE MENUS FROM THESE SUGGESTIONS:

Soups and Appetizers

1. Consomme' or clear broth

2. Vegetable soup— AVOID CREAM SOUPS

3. Gazpacho

4. Vegetable or fruit juice

Salads

1. Lettuce or spinach with fresh vegetables

2. If making a meal from a salad bar, exclude macaroni or potato salad or any other items heavily masked in mayonnaise or dressing. Choose a protein source such as cottage cheese, chopped egg, kidney or garbanzo beans. Remember, dressing on the side, and if no diet dressing is available, choose a thin dressing, since it goes further.

Sandwiches

1. Sliced turkey or chicken

2. Lean roast beef

3. Tuna (count mayonnaise)

4. Broiled hamburger (let fat drain on half of bun, then discard and eat other half of bun only)

Entrees

Avoid house specialties or chef's specials. These are usually heavily sauced. Select instead, meat, fish and poultry that is broiled, baked, roasted, steamed or poached.

Vegetables

Select steamed, boiled, baked or raw vegetables. For lightly stir-fried vegetables count "fat card"! Avoid vegetables prepared with sauces or butter.

Potatoes, Bread and Other Starches

Select baked or boiled potatoes; plain steamed rice. Pasta is fine with a simple tomato sauce or vegetables. Avoid butter, cream or cheese sauces. Hard rolls, bread sticks, steamed tortillas, plain breads, muffins and crackers are good selections.

Desserts

Fresh fruit is the best choice!

Beverages

Mineral water, iced tea, juice or wine spritzer. Remember to limit tea, coffee, and diet sodas to 2 servings daily.

HERE'S HOW:

ORIENTAL:

Ask for all food to be prepared without MSG.

Appetizers: Egg Drop soup, Won Ton soup, Hot and Sour soup, inside of Egg Roll!

Entrees: Ask for lightly stir-fried entrees with lots of vegetables. Avoid sweet and sour entrees or items that are breaded and fried. Plain rice, not fried!!

ITALIAN:

Choose a large tossed green salad to help your willpower.

Appetizer: Minnestrone soup

Entrees: Stay with pasta and vegetables, tomato or meat sauce. Stay away from Eggplant Parmesan and Lasagne, which are loaded with hidden calories. Choose either pasta or bread! Remember portions!

MEXICAN:

Keep your mits out of the chips!!!

Appetizers: Ask for a steamed corn tortilla to dip into the salsa. Gazpacho.

Entrees: Soft chicken tacos, vegetarian burritos, tostadas, tacos al Carbon are all fine. Watch portions of guacamole and sour cream. Count "fat" cards accordingly. Avoid refried beans, fried rice and fried tortillas for obvious reasons.

1. You shall have no other food programs except Deal-A-Meal.

2. You shall not bow down and worship any food.

3. You shall not call Deal-A-Meal by any other name (it's not Dial-A-Meal, Deal-A-Card, Dial-A-Dish, it's Deal-A-Meal).

4. Remember the workout day, for without it you will not lose your weight.

5. Honor your meat, fat, vege, fruit, bread, dairy, freebie and joker cards so that your days may be long on the land.

6. You shall not murder your Deal-A-Meal cards.

7. You shall not commit foodulterey, which is eating more food portions than your Deal-A-Meal cards allow.

8. You shall not steal extra Deal-A-Meal cards.

9. You shall not bear false witness against your fellow Deal-a-Mealer.

10. You shall not covet tomorrow's Deal-A-Meal 'fat' cards today.

Even though you don't need a Deal-A-Meal kit to enjoy this cookbook, it is designed to be used with one.

So if you don't have a Deal-A-Meal kit, you can order one by sending a check or money order for $19.95 (add $1.50 for postage and handling) to:

Deal-A-Meal
9306 Civic Center Drive
Beverly Hills, CA 90210

You can speed delivery by calling toll-free 1-800-831-5000 and using your credit card when ordering. You can also order your Deal-A-Meal C.O.D. by calling the same toll-free number.

E ver since I started losing weight on
Deal-A-Meal, I've had more energy
and never once felt deprived. I never
believed that I could lose weight and eat
good, healthy, great tasting food. I always
thought that I would have to starve myself
or constantly feel deprived. For the first
time in my life, I know that's not true.
Thank you, Richard Simmons and thank
you, Deal-A-Meal. You have changed
my life.

                    Celia Powell

GOOD MORNING!

There are not too many of us who want to get up early and prepare complicated breakfasts. So I suggest that you use the breakfast recipes that are more simple on weekdays and save the ones that are a bit harder for more fun and variety on weekends. We've marked the breakfasts that are easy to prepare with the caption, "Easy Breakfast" (how clever!). You can even entertain your friends with a "Deal-A-Meal" breakfast as a brunch and they'll never know it, unless you tell. We promise we won't!

Remember, if you have tea or coffee in the morning you're limited to 2 cups a day and that includes diet sodas too! Start trying some of the many herb teas available. It's all a matter of training your taste buds to accept new ideas. Some herb teas are particularly good when iced.

You are, of course, allowed to drink fruit juice as a fruit serving, but you'll get more lasting satisfaction (and fiber) if you eat whole fruit. It's a good idea to drink some water before you drink juice. You're less likely to gulp it down. You should be savoring it, as you would a fruit.

When choosing a sensible cereal, a good general rule to follow is this: the shorter the ingredient list, the less processed the cereal. Check the nutrition information for the fiber and sodium content. Bran type cereals contain the most fiber and shredded wheat is low in sodium.

Keep track of your dairy cards. If you use low-fat milk in your tea or coffee, measure it a few times so you'll know exactly how much you have left for your cereal. If you want to be frugal with your "fat" cards, switch to non-fat milk!

Well, enough said, let's make breakfast.

For perfect eggs every time, try these methods:

POACHED

1. Heat water about 1 1/2 inches deep in shallow straight-sided pan.
2. Using a safety pin or Egg piercer, pierce egg in round end of shell. Using a spoon, roll egg (still in shell) back and forth in boiling water about 10 times. Remove from water.
3. Reduce heat so water is barely simmering. Gently break egg into water. Cook about 3 minutes or to desired doneness. White should be firm and yolk still runny. Lift egg out with spatula and drain on a paper towel.

SCRAMBLED

1. Break egg (s) into mixing bowl and add two tablespoons non-fat milk for each egg.
2. Heat an appropriate size non stick skillet over medium heat.
3. Whisk egg (s) just to combine and pour into heated pan. Immediately lower heat and allow eggs to cook slowly and gently.
4. Lift and turn as setting occurs, keeping mixture in large soft masses.
5. Remove pan from heat just before done. Generated heat will complete cooking.

Low heat and slow cooking ensures tenderness of cooked eggs.

HARD COOKED

1. Use a safety pin or egg piercer and pierce egg (s) in round egg of shell. Place in saucepan and cover with cold water.
2. Heat until water is boiling. Remove pan from heat. Cover and let stand 20 minutes.
3. Plunge eggs immediately into cold water to prevent discoloration of the yolks. Crack shells. They will remove easily under cold running water.

OMELETS

1. Break egg (s) into mixing bowl and add 1 tablespoon non-fat milk or water for each egg used.
2. Heat an appropriate size non-stick skillet over medium flame.
3. Whisk egg (s) until thoroughly blended, but not foamy. Pour into heated pan. Tilt pan to evenly distribute egg mixture. As egg cooks gently push mixture towards center and lift sides with spatula to allow uncooked mixture to run underneath. When egg is set and lightly browned on bottom, shake pan to loosen omelet and fold in half. Slide out of pan.

BERRY SHAKE

MENU

- BERRY SHAKE
- 1/2 bagel, toasted
- 1 tablespoon cream cheese
- 1 cup black coffee or tea

INGREDIENTS

Berry shake
1/2 cup evaporated skim milk
1/2 cup fresh or frozen
unsweetened strawberries
1 teaspoon <u>each</u> honey and vanilla

DIRECTIONS

In blender combine all ingredients and blend until thick and smooth.

Makes 1 serving.

1 BREAD   1 DAIRY   1 FAT   1 FRUIT

B-2

281
CALORIES

'FRUIT SALAD' SMOOTHIE

MENU

- 1 serving 'FRUIT SALAD' SMOOTHIE
- 1/2 bagel toasted and spread with
- 1 tablespoon cream cheese
- 1 cup black coffee or tea

Makes 4 servings

INGREDIENTS

'Fruit Salad' Smoothie
- *1 ripe medium peach*
- *3/4 cup fresh or frozen strawberries*
- *1/2 banana peeled*
- *2 cups chilled evaporated skim milk*
- *4 teaspoons frozen orange juice concentrate*
- *1 teaspoon vanilla*
- *4 to 6 ice cubes*
- *Cinnamon (optional)*

DIRECTIONS

1. In blender combine all ingredients except ice and cinnamon.
2. With blender running, add ice cubes one at a time.
3. Divide Smoothie into 4 chilled glasses and sprinkle with cinnamon if desired.

DEAL-A-MEAL CARDS USED

 1 BREAD 1 DAIRY 1 FAT 1 FRUIT

246
CALORIES

BIG COFFEE CHILL

MENU

- 6 frozen grapes
- BIG COFFEE CHILL
- 1 slice whole wheat toast with
- 2 teaspoons diet jam

INGREDIENTS

Big Coffee Chill
- *1 cup chilled low-fat milk*
- *1 1/2 teaspoons instant coffee*
- *1 1/2 teaspoons sugar*
- *1 teaspoon vanilla*
- *1/8 teaspoon cinnamon*
- *4 to 6 ice cubes*

DIRECTIONS

1. In blender, combine all ingredients except ice cubes.
2. With blender running, add ice cubes one at a time.
3. Continue blending until smooth.

Makes 1 serving.

Tip: Frozen grapes take so much longer to eat, that you feel you are getting more than you really are.

D E A L - A - M E A L   C A R D S   U S E D

1 BREAD   1 DAIRY   1 FAT   1 FRUIT   1 JOKER

237

CALORIES

PIÑA COLADA SMOOTHIE

MENU
- PIÑA COLADA SMOOTHIE
- 1/2 English muffin with
- 2 teaspoons diet jam
- 1 cup black coffee or tea

INGREDIENTS
Piña Colada Smoothie
- *1/2 cup chilled evaporated skim milk*
- *1/2 teaspoon coconut extract*
- *1/4 ripe banana, peeled and frozen*
- *1/4 cup pineapple chunks, frozen*
- *2 to 3 ice cubes*

DIRECTIONS
1. In blender, combine evaporated skim milk and extract.
2. With blender running, add frozen banana and pineapple pieces a few at a time.
3. Add ice cubes one at a time.
4. Blend until smooth.

Makes 1 serving.

D E A L - A - M E A L   C A R D S   U S E D

 1 BREAD   1 DAIRY   1 FRUIT   1 JOKER

183
CALORIES

CEREAL WITH FRUIT

MENU

- 1 glass warm water with lemon juice
- 1/2 cup unfrosted cereal with
- 1/4 cup blueberries and 1/4 banana, sliced
- 1 cup non-fat milk or 1/2 cup non-fat milk and 1/2 cup plain non-fat yogurt
- 1 cup black coffee or tea

Note: Cut 1/4 banana before peeling. Protect cut surface of unused portion with plastic wrap.

D E A L - A - M E A L   C A R D S   U S E D

1 BREAD   1 DAIRY   1 FRUIT

B-6

262
CALORIES

OATMEAL WITH APPLE

MENU

- 1 glass warm water with lemon juice
- 1/2 cup cooked oatmeal with
- 1 small apple, chopped Dash cinnamon, and/ or orange zest to taste
- 1 cup low-fat milk
- 1 cup black coffee or tea

Makes 1 serving.

Note: You can buy orange zest in the seasonings section of the market, or make your own, by finely grating the orange part of the skin of an orange. (Be sure to wash the orange first.)

Variation: Use 1/2 apple and 1 tablespoon raisins instead of 1 apple.

D E A L - A - M E A L   C A R D S   U S E D

 1 BREAD   1 DAIRY   1 FAT   1 FRUIT

311

CALORIES

HAPPY TRAILS GRANOLA

MENU

- 1 glass warm water with lemon juice
- 1/2 cup HAPPY TRAILS GRANOLA
- 1 cup low-fat milk
- 1 cup black coffee or tea

INGREDIENTS

Happy Trails Granola
- *4 cups uncooked oatmeal*
- *1 cup wheat germ*
- *1 cup unprocessed bran*
- *6 tablespoons brown sugar*
- *3/4 cup (12 tablespoons) raisins*

DIRECTIONS

1. Preheat oven to 350 degrees.
2. In large shallow baking pan, mix all ingredients except raisins.
3. Bake 30 minutes, stirring every 5 to 10 minutes.
4. Remove from oven and stir in raisins.
5. Cool, then store in air-tight container.

Makes 12 (1/2 cup) servings.

Note: Add your own favorite spices as desired, such as cinnamon, nutmeg, allspice, cloves, or ginger. Add small amounts to each single serving, until you find the combination you like best.

D E A L - A - M E A L   C A R D S   U S E D

2 BREAD   1 DAIRY   1 FAT   1 FRUIT

196

CALORIES

CANTALOUPE WITH ENGLISH MUFFIN

MENU

- 1 glass warm water with lemon juice
- 1/4 cantaloupe with
- 1/4 cup low-fat cottage cheese
- 1/2 raisin-flavored English muffin, toasted and spread with
- 2 teaspoons diet jam
- 1 cup black coffee or tea

Variation: To make cantaloupe chop suey, cut cantaloupe into cubes and mix with cottage cheese. Toss with cinnamon to taste.

Tip: To freeze bagels or English muffins, stack halves so cut surfaces all face up. This makes it easy to separate frozen halves.

D E A L - A - M E A L   C A R D S   U S E D

34   1 BREAD   1 DAIRY   1 FRUIT   1 JOKER

209
CALORIES

PEANUT BUTTER BENEDICT

MENU
- 1 glass warm water with lemon juice
- PEANUT BUTTER BENEDICT
- 1 cup non-fat milk

INGREDIENTS
Peanut Butter Benedict
- *1 rice cake*
- *1 teaspoon peanut butter*
- *1/2 banana, sliced*

DIRECTIONS
Spread rice cake with peanut butter and arrange banana slices over top.

Makes 1 serving.

Tip: Toast rice cake to make it taste extra fresh and crispy

D E A L - A - M E A L   C A R D S   U S E D

1 DAIRY   1 FRUIT   2 JOKERS

322
CALORIES

SWEET PETZA

MENU

- 1 glass warm water with lemon juice
- 1 medium peach
- SWEET PETZA
- 1 cup non-fat milk

INGREDIENTS

Sweet Petza
- *1 slice wholewheat bread, toasted*
- *1 teaspoon peanut butter*
- *2 teaspoons diet jam*
- *1 ounce sliced low-fat mozzarella cheese*

DIRECTIONS

1. Preheat broiler. Spread toast with peanut butter and jam.
2. Top with cheese and place under broiler until cheese melts.

Makes 1 serving.

 1 BREAD 1 MEAT 1 DAIRY 1 FRUIT 2 JOKERS

349
CALORIES

BAGEL WITH 'CREAM' CHEESE AND TOMATO

MENU

- 1 glass warm water
  with lemon juice
- 1/3 cup orange juice
- 1 bagel toasted and
  spread with
- 2 tablespoons (1-ounce)
  Neufchatel cheese
- 1 tomato, sliced
- 1 cup non-fat milk

2 BREAD   1 MEAT   1 VEGE   1 DAIRY   1 FRUIT

157
CALORIES

RAISIN DANISH

MENU

- 1 glass warm water with lemon juice
- 1/2 cup strawberries
- RAISIN DANISH
- 1 cup black coffee or tea

INGREDIENTS

Raisin Danish
- *1 slice raisin bread*
- *1/4 cup low-fat cottage cheese*
- *1 teaspoon brown sugar*
- *1/4 teaspoon cinnamon*
- *1/8 teaspoon almond extract (optional)*

DIRECTIONS

1. Toast raisin bread.
2. Preheat broiler.
3. In small bowl, combine remaining ingredients.
4. Spread over raisin toast.
5. Place under broiler until hot and lightly browned.

Makes 1 serving.

Note: Be sure to choose plain raisin bread, not frosted! Let your conscience be your guide!

    1 BREAD   1 DAIRY   1 FRUIT

DUTCH APPLE YOGURT

MENU

- 1 glass warm water with lemon juice
- DUTCH APPLE YOGURT
- 1 slice wholewheat toast
- 1 teaspoon butter or margarine
- 1 cup black coffee or tea

INGREDIENTS

Dutch Apple Yogurt
1 cup plain non-fat yogurt
1/4 cup unsweetened applesauce
1 1/2 teaspoons brown sugar
1/4 teaspoon each vanilla and cinnamon

DIRECTIONS

1. In serving bowl, combine all ingredients. Mix thoroughly.

Makes 1 serving.

Tip: Why not make this a totally spicy breakfast and enjoy a spicy cinnamon-flavored herb tea.

D E A L · A · M E A L   C A R D S   U S E D

 1 BREAD   1 DAIRY   1 FAT   1 FRUIT

252
CALORIES

LA BAMBA QUESADILLA

MENU
- 1 glass warm water with lemon juice
- 1/3 cup orange juice
- LA BAMBA QUESADILLA
- 1 cup black coffee or tea

40

 1 BREAD   1 MEAT   2 FAT   1 FRUIT

La Bamba Quesadilla

- *1 (8-inch) wholewheat tortilla*
- *1 ounce Jack cheese*
- *1/8 avocado, mashed*
- *Salsa (optional)*

1. Using tongs, heat tortilla briefly over gas flame (see note) to soften. Grate cheese over tortilla.
2. Slide under preheated broiler or heat in microwave just until cheese melts.
3. Spread avocado over half of tortilla and add salsa if desired.
4. Fold other half of tortilla over filling to enclose. Cut in wedges.

Makes 1 serving.

Note: When I was in Mexico, I saw someone doing this. Turn on gas flame and place tortilla directly on burner. Turn tortilla several times with tongs. Alternately, heat tortilla in hot skillet, or in microwave just until warm and soft.

Tip: An avocado will easily keep in the refrigerator for more than a week if once you cut into it, you leave the pit intact and cover with plastic wrap.

170
CALORIES

CHIQUITA ON A SHINGLE

MENU
- 1 glass warm water with lemon juice
- CHIQUITA ON A SHINGLE
- 1 cup black coffee or tea

42   1 BREAD   1 FAT   1 FRUIT

Chiquita on a Shingle

- *1 slice wholewheat bread, toasted*
- *1 tablespoon cream cheese*
- *1/2 banana, sliced*
- *Cinnamon (optional)*

1. Spread toast with cream cheese.
2. Arrange banana slices over cheese.
3. Sprinkle with cinnamon to taste, if desired.

Makes 1 serving.

If you feed this to a child, or if you are a child yourself (and who isn't?) cut and arrange banana slices to form a face... preferably a cheerful one!

Tip: Gone are the days of peeling a whole banana, since 1/2 a banana equals 1 fruit. Just cut off portion required and cover remaining portion with plastic wrap.

To prevent bananas from all ripening at once (now that you'll be eating them more slowly) shop for them this way. Choose one that is green, one that is nearly ripe and one that is ripe.

If your bananas ripen faster than you planned, just peel, slice and bag them in 1 fruit portions in freezer. Use for delicious fruit smoothies. (see recipes B-2 and B-4)

166
CALORIES

CINNAMON HONEY MUFFIN

MENU
- 1 glass warm water with lemon juice
- 1/4 cup strawberries
- 1 CINNAMON HONEY MUFFIN
- 1 cup black coffee or tea

44   1 BREAD   1 FAT   1 FRUIT

Cinnamon Honey Muffins

- *3/4 cup unprocessed bran*
- *1 cup low-fat buttermilk*
- *1 egg, beaten*
- *1/4 cup honey*
- *1/4 cup vegetable oil*
- *1/2 cup raisins*
- *1/2 cup grated carrots*
- *1 1/4 cups sifted all- purpose flour*
- *1 teaspoon baking soda*
- *1/4 teaspoon salt*
- *1 teaspoon nutmeg*
- *1/2 teaspoon cinnamon*

1. Preheat oven to 425 degrees. Coat muffin pan with non-stick spray.
2. In medium bowl, combine bran, buttermilk, egg, honey, oil, raisins and carrots. Let stand 10 minutes.
3. In large bowl, sift together remaining ingredients.
4. Make well in center and add bran mixture. Stir just until dry ingredients are moistened. Batter should be lumpy. Do not overmix.
5. Spoon batter evenly into 12 muffin pans.
6. Bake 15 to 20 minutes or until tester comes out clean when inserted in center of muffin.

Makes 12 muffins.

Tip: These muffins can be frozen. When cool, wrap individually in foil

B-17

POACHED EGG WITH FRUIT

MENU
- 1 glass warm water with lemon juice
- 1/3 cup raspberries and 3 slices banana
- 1 Poached egg
- 1 slice wholewheat toast
- 1 teaspoon butter or margarine
- 1 cup black coffee or tea

46   1 BREAD   1 MEAT   1 FAT   1 FRUIT

SCRAMBLED EGG

MENU
- 1 glass warm water with lemon juice
- 1/2 grapefruit
- 1 SCRAMBLED EGG
- 1/2 English muffin with
- 2 teaspoons diet jam
- 3/4 cup non-fat milk

INGREDIENTS
Scrambled Egg
- *1 egg*
- *2 tablespoons non-fat milk*
- *Salt and pepper to taste*
- *1 tablespoon chopped parsley (optional)*

DIRECTIONS
1. In small bowl, whisk all ingredients.
2. Heat small non-stick skillet over medium heat. Pour egg into heated pan. Immediately lower heat.
3. Using spatula, lift and turn egg as it sets. Remove pan from heat just before done. (Generated heat will complete cooking.)

Makes 1 serving

Tip: Low heat and slow cooking ensure tenderness of cooked eggs.

D E A L · A - M E A L   C A R D S   U S E D

| 1 BREAD | 1 MEAT | 1 DAIRY | 1 FRUIT | 1 JOKER |

B-19

402
CALORIES

FRENCH TOAST WITH A PEEL

MENU

- FRENCH TOAST WITH A PEEL
- 3/4 cup non-fat milk

INGREDIENTS

French Toast with A Peel
- *1/2 very ripe banana, peeled*
- *2 tablespoons non-fat milk*
- *1/2 teaspoon each vanilla and cinnamon*
- *1 egg*
- *2 slices wholewheat bread*
- *2 tablespoons sour cream*

DIRECTIONS

1. Preheat oven to 350 degrees.
2. In blender, puree' all ingredients, except bread
3. Pour into shallow dish. Dip bread into mixtur until evenly coated, using all of mixture.
4. Arrange slices on non-stick baking sheet. Bake 15 minutes.
5. Serve, garnished with sour cream.

Makes 1 serving.

 2 BREAD   1 MEAT   1 DAIRY   1 FAT   1 FRUIT

314

CALORIES

THIS SPUD CAKE'S FOR YOU

MENU

- THIS SPUD CAKE'S FOR YOU with
- 1/2 cup applesauce and
- 2 tablespoons sour cream
- 1 cup black coffee or tea

Makes 1 serving.

INGREDIENTS

This Spud Cake's For You

- *1 extra small baking potato*
- *1 egg*
- *4 teaspoons all-purpose flour*
- *1/4 teaspoon salt*
- *Dash pepper*
- *1 tablespoon each grated onion and chopped parsley.*

DIRECTIONS

1. Peel and coarsely grate potato. Wrap in paper towel and squeeze to remove as much moisture as possible.
2. In small bowl, beat egg with remaining ingredients and stir in potato. Mix well.
3. Heat non-stick skillet over medium heat. Spoon mixture into pan to make 4 pancakes.
4. Cook until bottom is browned. Turn to brown other side.

D E A L · A · M E A L   C A R D S   U S E D

1 BREAD   1 MEAT   1 FAT   1 FRUIT

343
CALORIES

MELT-IN-YOUR-MOUTH WAFFLES

MENU
- 1 glass warm water with lemon juice
- 1 serving MELT-IN-YOUR-MOUTH WAFFLES
  with CINNAMON YOGURT CREME
- 1 cup black coffee or tea

D E A L - A - M E A L   C A R D S   U S E D

 2 BREAD   1 DAIRY   1 FAT   1 FRUIT

Melt-In-Your-Mouth Waffles with Cinnamon Yogurt Creme

- 1 3/4 cups sifted all-purpose flour
- 1 1/4 teaspoons baking powder
- 1/4 teaspoon baking soda
- 1 tablespoon sugar
- 1/4 teaspoon salt
- 1 egg yolk
- 1 1/2 cups low-fat buttermilk
- 5 teaspoons melted butter
- 2 egg whites
- Cinnamon Yogurt Creme (recipe follows)
- 1 1/2 cups blueberries

1. Preheat waffle iron. In large bowl, sift flour with baking powder, baking soda, sugar and salt. Set aside.
2. In medium bowl, beat egg yolk until light. Add buttermilk and melted butter.
3. Make well in center of dry ingredients and pour in liquid. Stir just until dry ingredients are moistened.
4. In separate bowl, beat egg whites until stiff, but not dry. Fold whites gently into batter.
5. Bake in waffle iron. To serve, place 2 waffles on each plate. Top with Cinnamon Yogurt Creme and sprinkle with blueberries.

Makes 6 servings.

Cinnamon Yogurt Creme

- 4 1/2 cups plain non-fat yogurt
- 3 tablespoons frozen apple juice concentrate, thawed
- 1 tablespoon vanilla
- 1 teaspoon cinnamon

In large bowl combine all ingredients.

Makes 6 servings.

JOHNNY APPLESEED PANCAKE

MENU

- 1 juice spritzer
- 1 serving JOHNNY APPLESEED PANCAKE
- 3/4 cup non-fat milk

1 MEAT   1 DAIRY   1 FAT   1 FRUIT   1 JOKER

Johnny Appleseed Pancake

- *1 small green apple*
- *1 tablespoon sugar*
- *1/2 teaspoon cinnamon*
- *2 teaspoons butter or margarine*
- *2 eggs, separated*
- *1/4 cup non-fat milk*
- *1 tablespoon all-purpose flour*
- *1/4 teaspoon each nutmeg and baking powder*

1. Preheat oven to 400 degrees. Peel, core and cut apple into thin slices.
2. In bowl, mix half of sugar with cinnamon and toss with apple slices.
3. In 9-inch non-stick oven-proof skillet melt butter. Arrange apple slices over bottom of skillet.
4. Cook over low heat about 5 minutes.
5. Meanwhile, in medium bowl beat egg whites until soft peaks form.
6. Add remaining sugar and continue to beat until firm and glossy.
7. In small bowl, beat together egg yolks, milk, flour, nutmeg and baking powder.
8. Fold yolk mixture into egg whites.
9. Pour batter over apples and spread evenly.
10. Bake 12 minutes. Invert onto heated serving plate and cut in wedges.

Makes 2 servings.

345
CALORIES

BLUEBERRY HILL PANCAKES

MENU
- 1 juice spritzer
- 1 serving BLUEBERRY HILL PANCAKES
- 1 serving YOGURT RICOTTA TOPPING
- 1 cup black coffee or tea

 1 BREAD
 1 MEAT
1 DAIRY
 1 FAT
 1 FRUIT
 1 JOKER

INGREDIENTS | DIRECTIONS

Blueberry Hill Pancakes

- 3/4 cup low-fat cottage cheese
- 3 eggs
- 1/2 cup sifted all-purpose flour
- 4 teaspoons vegetable oil
- 1 tablespoon sugar
- 1/2 teaspoon <u>each</u> vanilla and nutmeg
- 1 cup fresh or frozen blueberries
- Yogurt Ricotta Topping

1. In blender, combine all ingredients except blueberries and topping. Blend until smooth.
2. Add blueberries and blend 2 seconds more, just to break up blueberries slightly.
3. Preheat large non-stick skillet or griddle.
4. For each pancake, pour 1/4 cup batter onto hot griddle.
5. Cook pancakes until bubbles appear and edges look dry.
6. Turn and cook until other side is golden brown.
7. Serve with Yogurt Ricotta Topping.

Makes 4 servings.

INGREDIENTS | DIRECTIONS

Yogurt Ricotta Topping

- l cup plain non-fat yogurt
- 1/2 cup (4 ounces) part-skim ricotta cheese
- l tablespoon brown sugar
- l teaspoon vanilla

1. In small deep bowl, combine all ingredients.
2. Beat mixture with electric mixer until smooth and creamy.
3. (May be stored in refrigerater several days.) Beat with whisk, if desired, before serving.

Makes 4 servings.

469
CALORIES

HUEVOS RANCHEROS CHA CHA CHA

MENU

- 1/2 cup chilled grapefruit juice
- HUEVOS RANCHEROS CHA CHA CHA
- 1 cup black coffee or tea

56   2 BREAD   3 MEAT   2 FAT   1 FRUIT

Huevos Rancheros
Cha Cha Cha

- *1 egg*
- *2 tablespoons non-fat milk*
- *Salt and pepper to taste*
- *1/2 cup drained, cooked or canned pinto beans*
- *1 tablespoon chopped canned green chile*
- *1 (8 -inch) wholewheat tortilla*
- *1 ounce shredded Jack cheese*
- *1/8 avocado, sliced*
- *Salsa*

1. Preheat broiler. Scramble egg with milk and seasonings. See directions next to recipe B-1.
2. In small pan heat pinto beans with green chile.
3. Soften tortilla over gas flame or in microwave. See instructions with recipe B-14.
4. Place tortilla on oven-proof serving platter.
5. Spoon pinto beans and scrambled egg on tortilla. Sprinkle with cheese.
6. Place briefly under broiler until cheese starts to melt.
7. Garnish with avocado slices and serve with salsa.

Makes 1 serving.

Tip: Freeze grapefruit juice then blend so that it becomes thick and frosty like a margarita.

297
CALORIES

VEGETABLE SCRAMBLE

MENU
- 1/3 cup orange juice
- VEGETABLE SCRAMBLE
- 1 slice wholewheat toast spread with
  1 teaspoon butter or margarine
- 3/4 cup non-fat milk

DEAL - A - MEAL CARDS USED

58   1 BREAD   1 MEAT   1 VEGE   1 DAIRY   1 FAT   1 FRUIT

Vegetable Scramble

- *1/4 cup chopped mushrooms*
- *2 tablespoons chopped green onion*
- *1 tablespoon water or chicken broth*
- *1 egg*
- *2 tablespoons non-fat milk*
- *1/8 teaspoon each dried oregano and basil*
- *Salt and pepper to taste*
- *2 cherry tomatoes*

1. In small non-stick skillet, saute' mushrooms and onion in water until soft, and liquid has evaporated.
2. In small bowl, beat egg with milk and crushed herbs.
3. Add egg mixture to vegetables in skillet, reduce heat and stir gently until egg is set.
4. Garnish with tomatoes.

Makes 1 serving.

265
CALORIES

SWEET OMELET SOUFFLE'

MENU
- SWEET OMELET SOUFFLE´
- 1 serving YOGURT RICOTTA TOPPING
- Cafe' au lait with 3/4 cup non-fat milk

60   2 MEAT   1 DAIRY   1 FRUIT

Sweet Omelet Souffle'
- *1 egg, separated*
- *1 tablespoon water*
- *1 teaspoon sugar*
- *1/4 teaspoon vanilla*
- *1/4 cup sliced strawberries*
- *Yogurt Ricotta Topping (recipe follows)*

1. Preheat broiler. In small bowl, beat egg white with electric mixer until stiff peaks form. Set aside.
2. In separate small bowl, combine water, sugar, vanilla and egg yolk. Beat until very thick.
3. Preheat small non-stick oven-proof omelet pan over medium heat.
4. Fold yolk mixture into egg white. Pour mixture into heated omelet pan spreading evenly.
5. Cook omelet over medium heat 30 seconds. Reduce heat and cook without disturbing until omelet is almost set and lightly browned on bottom.
6. Place under broiler about 1 minute, or until top is lightly browned.
7. Arrange strawberries over half of omelet. Fold other half over to enclose fruit.
8. Slide omelet onto warmed serving plate and top with 1/4 of Yogurt Ricotta Topping.

Makes 1 serving.

Yogurt Ricotta Topping
- *1 cup plain non-fat yogurt*
- *1/2 cup (4 ounces) part-skim ricotta cheese*
- *1 tablespoon brown sugar*
- *1 teaspoon vanilla*

1. In small deep bowl, combine all ingredients.
2. Beat mixture with electric mixer until smooth and creamy.
3. (May be stored in refrigerater several days.) Beat with whisk, if desired, before serving.

Makes 4 servings.

GARDEN VEGE FRITTATA

MENU
- 1/2 Papaya with 3 tablespoons cottage cheese and wedge of lime
- 1 serving GARDEN VEGE FRITTATA
- 1/2 English muffin with 2 teaspoons diet jam
- 1 cup black coffee or tea

D E A L - A - M E A L   C A R D S   U S E D

1 BREAD   2 MEAT   1 VEGE   1 DAIRY   1 FAT   1 FRUIT   1 JOKER

GardenVege Frittata

- *1 cup diced zucchini*
- *3/4 cup thinly sliced carrot*
- *1/4 cup thinly sliced onion*
- *3 eggs, beaten*
- *1 cup plain, non-fat yogurt*
- *1 cup (4 ounces) shredded Jack cheese*
- *3 tablespoons grated Parmesan cheese*
- *2 tablespoons chopped parsley*
- *2 tablespoons all-purpose flour*
- *1/4 teaspoon each dried oregano and salt*
- *Dash each pepper and nutmeg*

1. Preheat oven to 350 degrees.
2. Steam or microwave zucchini, carrot and onion until just tender. Drain.
3. In medium bowl, combine remaining ingredients. Stir in steamed vegetables.
4. Pour vegetable mixture into shallow 1 1/2-to 2-quart casserole or baking pan coated with non-stick spray.
5. Bake, uncovered, 25 to 30 minutes or until knife inserted near center comes out clean.
6. Let stand 10 minutes before serving.

Makes 4 servings.

257
CALORIES

SWISS ALPS SANDWICH SOUFFLE'

MENU

- 1 juice spritzer
- 1 serving SWISS ALPS SANDWICH SOUFFLE´
- 1 cup black coffee or tea

DEAL-A-MEAL CARDS USED

64   1 BREAD   1 MEAT   1 DAIRY   1 FAT   1 JOKER

Swiss Alps Sandwich Souffle´

- *2 slices wholewheat bread*
- *Mustard*
- *1 (1-ounce) slice Swiss cheese*
- *1 egg*
- *1 cup non-fat milk*
- *1/4 cup low-fat cottage cheese*
- *1 teaspoon instant minced onion*
- *1/4 teaspoon each garlic powder, salt and pepper*

1. Preheat oven to 350 degrees. Spread both slices of bread with mustard.
2. Make sandwich with cheese. Cut into quarters.
3. Divide sandwich triangles into 2 small baking dishes and arrange with points up.
4. In small mixing bowl, beat egg with remaining ingredients and divide between baking dishes, thoroughly moistening bread.
5. Bake 30 to 40 minutes or until sandwiches are crisp and golden brown and custard is firm.

Makes 2 servings.

Tip: To keep sandwiches standing during cooking, secure with wooden pick. Remove before serving.

443
CALORIES

TOOTIE FROOTIE OMELET RATATOUILLE

MENU
- 1 juice spritzer
- 1 serving TOOTIE FROOTIE
- OMELET RATATOUILLE
- 1/2 English muffin spread with
- 1 1/2 teaspoons cream cheese
- 1 cup black coffee or tea

1 BREAD 3 MEAT   2 VEGE   1 FAT   1 FRUIT   1 JOKER

INGREDIENTS   DIRECTIONS

Tootie Frootie
- 1 *kiwifruit, peeled*
- 1/2 *papaya, peeled and seeded*
- 3/4 *cup strawberries*
- 1/2 *cup blueberries*
- *Fresh mint (optional)*

1. Cut kiwifruit and papaya into quarters lengthwise, then cut into wedge-shaped cubes.
2. In bowl combine with strawberries and blueberries.
3. Divide fruit equally among 4 serving bowls.
4. Garnish each with sprig of mint, if desired.

Makes 4 servings.

INGREDIENTS   DIRECTIONS

Omelet Ratatouille
- 2 *eggs*
- 2 *tablespoons water*
- 1/2 *ounce shredded Cheddar or Swiss cheese*
- 1 *serving Ratatouille Filling (recipe follows)*
- 1 1/2 *teaspoons grated Parmesan cheese*

1. Preheat small non-stick skillet over medium heat.
2. In small bowl, beat eggs with water. Pour into heated pan.
3. Tilt pan to evenly distribute egg mixture. Reduce heat slightly.
4. As eggs cook, gently push cooked portion toward center, lifting sides with spatula to allow uncooked portion to flow underneath.
5. When egg is almost set, sprinkle with cheese.
6. Cook until egg is set and lightly browned on bottom.
7. Spread Ratatouille Filling over half of omelet. Sprinkle with Parmesan.
8. Fold omelet in half to enclose filling and slide out of pan onto serving plate.

Makes 1 serving.

INGREDIENTS   DIRECTIONS

Ratatouille Filling
- 2 *cups peeled, cubed eggplant*
- 2 *teaspoons olive oil*
- 1 *clove garlic, minced*
- 1/2 *cup each chopped onion and green pepper*
- 1/2 *cup sliced mushrooms*
- 1/2 *cup peeled, seeded chopped tomato*
- 1/2 *teaspoon each dried oregano and basil*
- 1/4 *teaspoon coarsely ground pepper*
- 2 *teaspoons lemon juice, or to taste*
- 2 *tablespoons chopped parsley*

1. Steam or microwave eggplant until tender.
2. Drain on paper towel. Set aside.
3. In medium non-stick skillet, heat olive oil.
4. Add garlic, onion and green pepper and saute' until vegetables start to soften, about 5 minutes.
5. Add eggplant, mushrooms, tomato and seasonings. Cover and reduce heat.
6. Simmer until vegetables are tender, about 10 minutes. Stir in lemon juice and parsley.
7. Set aside and keep warm.

Makes 4 servings.

Note: Ratatouille Filling can be made ahead of time and reheated.

268
CALORIES

PUFF THE MAGIC PIE

MENU
- 1/2 cup mixed blueberries and raspberries
- 1 serving PUFF THE MAGIC PIE
- 1 cup black coffee or tea

DEAL-A-MEAL CARDS USED

 1 BREAD   1 MEAT   1 VEGE   1 FAT   1 FRUIT

Puff The Magic Pie

- *3 cups mixed, chopped vegetables such as broccoli, carrots, mushrooms, zucchini and tomato*
- *1/2 teaspoon dried Italian herbs*
- *Dash pepper*
- *2 tablespoons butter or margarine*
- *2 eggs*
- *1 cup low-fat milk*
- *1 cup sifted all-purpose flour*
- *1/4 teaspoon salt*
- *1 cup (4 ounces) shredded Jack cheese*

1. Preheat oven to 425 degrees. Steam or microwave vegetables until just tender. Drain.
2. Toss in bowl with herbs and pepper. Set aside.
3. Put butter in 10-inch pie plate and set in oven until butter is melted.
4. In medium bowl, beat eggs. Add milk and beat until well blended.
5. Add flour and salt and beat until batter is smooth.
6. Pour batter into heated pie plate.
7. Spread vegetables evenly over batter to within 1 inch of edge. Sprinkle with cheese.
8. Bake 30 minutes or until brown and puffy. Serve, cut in wedges.

Makes 6 servings.

340
CALORIES

BLUEBERRY BREAD PUDDING

MENU
- BLUEBERRY BREAD PUDDING
- 1 cup black coffee or tea

INGREDIENTS
Blueberry Bread Pudding
- *1 slice wholewheat bread*
- *1 cup low-fat buttermilk*
- *1 egg*
- *1 tablespoon sugar*
- *1/2 teaspoon vanilla*
- *1/2 cup frozen, unsweetened blueberries*

DIRECTIONS
1. Preheat oven to 350 degrees.
2. In blender or food processor, combine all ingredients, except blueberries. Process until blended.
3. Stir in blueberries.
4. Pour mixture into 1-pint baking dish.
5. Bake 1 hour or until pudding is set.

Makes 1 serving.

Make this when you make dinner and you'll have an easy ready-to-go breakfast the next morning.

 1 BREAD 1 MEAT 1 DAIRY 2 FRUIT

When I was fat I hated myself and had no self- esteem. I grew up from a fat child to a fat adult. I tried every quick weight loss diet but always gained the weight back.

I heard Richard Simmons speak about Deal-A-Meal and I knew I had found a food program I could live with. Deal-A-Meal is great because I can see exactly what I eat by looking at the cards I play. There's no guess work involved and I now have control over my eating. I love the person I've become now. I'm more positive and more energetic. Thank you, Richard, from the bottom of my heart.

Judy Pendley

"WHAT'S FOR LUNCH?"

It's lunch time and you can either have a stale peanut butter and jelly sandwich or a steaming hot broiled chicken with red potato salad. Which would you choose? If you chose the stale peanut butter and jelly sandwich I suggest you skip this section of the book. However, if you picked the broiled chicken with red potato salad, I think you're just going to love this chapter.

Lunch time does not have to be boring. The lunch meals in this chapter are simple to prepare and even better to eat. While some of these lunch menus have been specially designed for brown bagging, all of them are portable if you have a good thermos and a few sturdy containers. There is no excuse for getting into a rut of eating boring unhealthy food, whether it be at work, school or home. Remember, all it takes is a little weekend planning and you can be set for the entire week.

TABLE OF CONTENTS

355
CALORIES

CREAMY TATER SOUP AND SALAD

MENU
- 1 serving CREAMY TATER SOUP
- YOU MUST BE YOLKING SALAD with
- lettuce and soda crackers
- 3/4 cup strawberries
- Mineral water

D E A L - A - M E A L   C A R D S   U S E D

 1 BREAD   1 MEAT   1 VEGE   1 DAIRY   1 FAT   1 FRUIT   1 JOKER

INGREDIENTS

Creamy Tater Soup
- 4 cups defatted chicken broth
- 1 cup chopped onion
- 3 cups chopped celery, including leaves
- 2 small potatoes peeled and cubed
- 1/2 teaspoon salt
- Dash cayenne pepper
- 1 cup low-fat milk

DIRECTIONS

1. In large saucepan, combine all ingredients except milk. Cook until vegetables are very tender, about 10 minutes. Cool slightly.
2. Transfer to blender and blend until smooth. Stir in milk.
3. At this point, may be stored in refrigerator up to 1 week.
4. Heat before serving.

Makes 4 servings.

INGREDIENTS

You Must Be Yolking Salad
- 1 hard-cooked egg, peeled and chopped
- 3 tablespoons low-fat cottage cheese
- 1 teaspoon chopped parsley
- 1/2 teaspoon curry powder
- Dash each salt and pepper
- 1 tablespoon diet mayonnaise
- Romaine lettuce leaves
- 2 soda crackers or
- 1 breadstick

DIRECTIONS

1. In small bowl, combine all ingredients.
2. Cover and keep chilled.
3. Serve mounded in lettuce leaves, with soda crackers or breadstick.

Makes 1 serving.

218
CALORIES

SALAD OF THE SEA

MENU
- 1 (6 ounce) can vegetable juice, frozen
- SALAD OF THE SEA
- 2 bread sticks

D E A L - A - M E A L   C A R D S   U S E D

1 BREAD   2 MEAT   1 VEGE   1 FAT

Salad Of The Sea

- *2 ounces cooked fish, cooled and flaked*
- *1 tablespoon diet mayonnaise*
- *1/4 teaspoon <u>each</u> Dijon mustard and lemon pepper seasoning*
- *1 tablespoon diced celery*
- *1 teaspoon chopped parsley*
- *Lettuce leaves*
- *Cucumber slices*
- *Alfalfa sprouts*
- *1 small tomato, sliced*

1. In small bowl, combine fish, mayonnaise, mustard, lemon pepper, celery and parsley.
2. Serve on lettuce leaves with cucumber, sprouts and tomato.

Makes 1 serving.

Tip: Freezing a can of vegetable juice to take along in your brown bag lunch, will keep everything chilled while it thaws, ready to drink at noon.

PASTA INSALATA

MENU

- PASTA INSALATA
- 1 bread roll
- 1 small orange or apple
- Diet soda

D E A L - A - M E A L C A R D S U S E D

 2 BREAD

 1 MEAT

 2 VEGE

 1 FAT

 1 FRUIT

Pasta Insalata
- *1/2 cup cooked, drained pasta*
- *1 cup cut-up steamed vegetables, such as zucchini, broccoli, yellow squash, onion, carrot and red pepper*
- *2 tablespoons lo-cal dressing*
- *3 tablespoons grated Parmesan cheese*
- *1 tablespoon chopped parsley*

1. In bowl combine all ingredients.
2. Toss well and chill.

Makes 1 serving.

394

CALORIES

SCANDANAVIAN SALMON SOUFFLE'

MENU
- SCANDANAVIAN SALMON SOUFFLE'
- Freebie Salad
- 2 teaspoons lo-cal dressing
- 1 small nectarine
- Herb tea

1 BREAD   2 MEAT   1 DAIRY   1 FAT   1 FRUIT

Scandanavian Salmon Souffle'

- *1 slice wholewheat bread*
- *1/4 cup drained, flaked canned salmon*
- *1 egg, beaten*
- *1/2 cup evaporated skim milk*
- *1 tablespoon <u>each</u> chopped onion, celery and parsley*
- *1 teaspoon lemon juice*
- *1/4 teaspoon dried dill weed*
- *Dash pepper*
- *1/4 teaspoon Worcestershire sauce*

1. Preheat oven to 350 degrees. Coat small souffle' dish with non-stick spray.
2. In bowl break bread into small pieces.
3. Mix in remaining ingredients.
4. Pour mixture into prepared souffle' dish.
5. Bake 35 minutes or until knife inserted in center comes out clean.

Makes 1 serving.

Note: This isn't a collapsible kind of souffle' (the kind that must be eaten seconds after it comes out of the oven!) The bread in this makes it sturdy enough to take to work and reheat in the micro-wave.

280
CALORIES

1 POTATO, 2 POTATO PICNIC SALAD WITH EASY BROILED CHICKEN

MENU

- 1 serving 1 POTATO, 2 POTATO PICNIC SALAD
- 1 serving EASY BROILED CHICKEN
- 1/4 Cantaloupe
- Iced Tea

D E A L - A - M E A L   C A R D S   U S E D

 1 BREAD

 2 MEAT

 1 FAT

 1 FRUIT

INGREDIENTS	DIRECTIONS

1 Potato, 2 Potato Picnic Salad

Dressing:
- 1 tablespoon vegetable oil
- 1 tablespoon white wine vinegar
- 1/2 teaspoon Dijon mustard
- 1/4 teaspoon sugar
- Salt and pepper to taste

Salad:
- 4 small red potatoes, cooked and drained
- 6 walnuts, coarsely chopped
- 2 green onions, sliced diagonally
- 2 tablespoons chopped fresh dill <u>or</u> 1 teaspoon dried dill weed
- Lettuce leaves

1. In medium bowl mix dressing ingredients.
2. Cube hot potatoes and add to bowl with dressing. Toss. Cool, tossing occasionally.
3. Add nuts, onions and dill. Toss again. Serve at room temperature in lettuce lined bowl.

Makes 4 servings.

INGREDIENTS	DIRECTIONS

Easy Broiled Chicken
- 4 small chicken thighs, skinned
- Garlic powder
- Italian herbs
- Paprika

1. Preheat broiler. Arrange chicken pieces in one layer in broiler pan.
2. Sprinkle with seasonings.
3. Broil 10 minutes.
4. Turn and season on other side. Broil another 10 minutes, or until tender.

Makes 4 servings.

Tip: To test for doneness, pierce a fleshy part with wooden skewer. If juices are clear, chicken is done.

Note: Try other seasonings for variation, such as Dijon mustard, rosemary and lemon juice, but always include paprika as this gives color to the chicken. In fact, it is almost impossible to tell that the skin has been removed.

89

283
CALORIES

WHAT'S UP DOC SOUP

MENU
- 1 serving WHAT'S UP DOC SOUP
- Freebie Salad
- 2 tablespoons lo-cal dressing
- 2 tablespoons low-fat cottage cheese
- 2 bread sticks
- 6 frozen grapes
- Iced tea

D E A L - A - M E A L   C A R D S   U S E D

 1 BREAD
 1 VEGE
 1 DAIRY
2 FAT
 1 FRUIT
 1 JOKER

What's Up Doc Soup

- 2 teaspoons butter or margarine
- 1 small clove garlic, crushed
- 1/2 cup thinly sliced onion
- 1 1/2 cups finely grated carrot
- 2 cups defatted chicken broth
- 1 teaspoon sugar
- 1/2 teaspoon orange zest
- 1/4 cup orange juice
- 1/2 cup evaporated skim milk
- 2 teaspoons cornstarch
- 1 tablespoon cold water
- Salt and pepper
- Chopped parsley and grated carrots (optional)

1. In small saucepan, melt butter. Add garlic and onion and saute' until onion is translucent.
2. Add carrot, broth and sugar. Simmer 10 minutes, or until carrot is tender. Puree'.
3. Stir in orange zest, juice, and milk
4. Combine cornstarch and water and stir into soup. Continue to stir over medium heat until soup has thickened slightly.
5. Add salt and pepper to taste. Garnish with parsley and carrot, if desired.

Makes 2 servings.

355
CALORIES

ROMAN HOLIDAY SOUP

MENU
- 1 serving ROMAN HOLIDAY SOUP
- 1 serving Crusty Italian Bread
- 1 cup black coffee or tea

D E A L - A - M E A L   C A R D S   U S E D

2 BREAD   1 MEAT   1 VEGE   1 FAT

Roman Holiday Soup

- *1 cup chopped onion*
- *1 1/2 cups sliced carrots*
- *1 tablespoon olive oil*
- *1 1/2 cups sliced green beans*
- *1/2 cup uncooked macaroni*
- *6 cups defatted chicken broth*
- *1/2 teaspoon salt*
- *1/4 cup tomato paste*
- *2 cloves garlic, crushed*
- *2 tablespoons chopped fresh basil or 1 1/2 teaspoons dried basil*
- *6 tablespoons grated Parmesan cheese*
- *1 tablespoon vegetable oil*
- *1 tablespoon cornstarch*
- *2 tablespoons cold water*
- *2 cups drained, canned or cooked white beans*

1. In large saucepan, saute' onion and carrots in olive oil until onion is translucent.
2. Add green beans, macaroni, broth and salt. Bring to boil and simmer about 10 minutes or until vegetables are tender and macaroni is cooked.
3. In medium bowl, combine tomato paste, garlic, basil and cheese. Slowly whisk in oil.
4. Stir mixture into soup pot. Dissolve cornstarch in water and stir into soup over medium heat until soup has thickened slightly.
5. Stir in white beans and heat through.

Makes 6 servings.

393
CALORIES

BOSTON CLAM CHOWDER

MENU
- BOSTON CLAM CHOWDER
- 6 saltines
- Freebie Salad
- 2 tablespoons lo-cal dressing
- Iced tea or diet soda

D E A L - A - M E A L   C A R D S   U S E D

 2 BREAD   1 MEAT   1 VEGE   1 DAIRY 2 FAT   1 JOKER

Boston Clam Chowder

- 1/3 cup <u>each</u> chopped onion, sliced celery and sliced leek
- 1 cup defatted chicken broth
- 1 small red potato, diced
- 1 cup low-fat milk
- 5 drained, canned clams, chopped
- Salt and pepper to taste
- 1 cup shredded spinach
- Freshly grated nutmeg (optional)

1. In medium saucepan, saute' onion, celery and leek in small amount of broth, about 5 minutes.
2. Add potato and remaining broth. Bring to boil and simmer covered, about 10 minutes or until potato is tender.
3. Stir in remaining ingredients. Heat without boiling.

Makes 1 serving.

466
CALORIES

TOMATO LACE QUICHE

MENU

- 1 serving TOMATO LACE QUICHE with
- 4 steamed asparagus spears sprinkled with lemon juice
- 1 small apple
- 1 cup black coffee or tea

 1 BREAD   2 MEAT   1 VEGE   1 DAIRY   1 FAT   1 FRUIT

Tomato Lace Quiche

Crust:
- *2 cups cooked rice*
- *1 egg, beaten*
- *1 tablespoon grated Parmesan cheese*

Filling:
- *1/4 cup chopped green onion*
- *1 teaspoon butter or margarine*
- *1 cup peeled, seeded and coarsely chopped tomatoes*
- *3/4 cup (3 ounces) shredded Swiss cheese*
- *2 tablespoons grated Parmesan cheese*
- *3 eggs*
- *1 cup evaporated skim milk*
- *1/2 cup low-fat cottage cheese*
- *1 teaspoon Italian mixed herbs, or 1/2 teaspoon each oregano and basil*
- *1/4 teaspoon salt*
- *1/8 teaspoon coarsely ground pepper*

1. Preheat oven to 425 degrees.
2. In bowl, combine rice, egg and Parmesan.
3. Press firmly into deep (10-inch) quiche dish or pie pan to form a crust.
4. Bake 3 minutes. Remove from oven.
5. Reduce oven temperature to 350 degrees.
6. In skillet saute' onion in butter, stirring until onion is soft. Remove from heat. Stir in tomato and cheeses. Spoon mixture into rice crust.
7. In large bowl beat together remaining ingredients. Pour mixture into rice crust.
8. Bake 35 minutes or until just set.
9. Let stand 5 minutes, then slice to serve.

Makes 4 servings.

Note: In case you wondered, the name for this recipe came about because the crust looks like lace, when cooked.

272
CALORIES

SALMON WITH A VIEW

MENU
- SALMON WITH A VIEW with
- COLESLAW
- Diet Soda

102   1 BREAD   1 MEAT   1 VEGE   1 FAT   1 FRUIT

INGREDIENTS	DIRECTIONS

Salmon with a View

- 1/4 *cup drained and flaked, canned salmon*
- *1 tablespoon diet mayonnaise*
- *1 slice wholewheat bread*
- *Lettuce leaf*
- *Cucumber and tomato slices*
- *1 sprig fresh dill*

1. Mix salmon with mayonnaise and spread on bread over lettuce leaf.
2. Arrange cucumber, tomato slices and dill on top.

Makes 1 serving.

INGREDIENTS	DIRECTIONS

Coleslaw

- *1 1/2 cups finely shredded cabbage*
- *1/4 cup grated carrot*
- *1/4 cup thinly chopped red onion*
- *1/4 cup chopped parsley*
- *3 tablespoons raisins*
- *1 1/2 teaspoons sugar*
- *Salt and pepper to taste*
- *1/4 cup rice vinegar*

1. In medium bowl, combine cabbage, carrot, onion, parsley and raisins.
2. In small bowl, stir together remaining ingredients until sugar has dissolved. Pour over cabbage mixture. Toss and chill.

Makes 2 servings.

157

CALORIES

HONG KONG CHICKEN SALAD

MENU
- 1 serving HONG KONG CHICKEN SALAD
- 1/2 cup Mandarin orange segments in own juice
- 1 cup tea

D E A L - A - M E A L   C A R D S   U S E D

 1 MEAT 1 VEGE 1 FAT 1 FRUIT

Hong Kong Chicken Salad

Dressing:
- 1 1/2 tablespoons rice vinegar
- 4 teaspoons salad oil
- 2 teaspoons dark sesame oil
- 1/4 teaspoon salt
- 1/8 teaspoon coarsely ground pepper
- 1 teaspoon sugar

Salad:
- 6 ounces cooked, boned and skinned chicken, shredded
- 3 cups shredded Romaine lettuce
- 1 cup fresh bean sprouts
- 3 to 4 green onions slivered lengthwise and cut into 1 inch pieces

1. For dressing, ahead of time, shake together dressing ingredients in tightly sealed container. Chill.
2. Just before serving, in large salad bowl, toss together chilled salad ingredients and dressing.

Makes 6 servings.

298
CALORIES

PRESTO PIZZA

MENU

- Freebie Salad
- 2 tablespoons lo-cal dressing
- 1 serving PRESTO PIZZA
- 1 cup black coffee or tea

106

 2 BREAD

 1 MEAT

 1 VEGE

 2 FAT

Presto Pizza

Crust:
- *1 cup sifted all-purpose flour*
- *1 teaspoon baking powder*
- *1/4 teaspoon dried oregano*
- *1 tablespoon butter or margarine*
- *3 to 5 tablespoons water*

Topping:
- *1/4 cup prepared, all-natural spaghetti sauce*
- *2 cups thinly-sliced vegetables such as onions, mushrooms, tomatoes, green pepper, zucchini*
- *1/2 teaspoon dried oregano*
- *3 ounces shredded low-fat mozzarella cheese*

1. Preheat oven to 400 degrees.
2. For crust, in bowl, combine flour, baking powder and oregano.
3. With finger tips, work in butter until mixture resembles coarse oatmeal.
4. Stir quickly with fork, while slowly pouring in enough water to make soft dough.
5. On lightly floured board, knead dough about 8 times.
6. Roll dough to fit 10-inch pie or pizza pan. Press dough into pan.
7. Spread with spaghetti sauce.
8. Arrange vegetables over crust. Sprinkle with oregano and cheese.
9. Bake 30 minutes.

Makes 3 servings.

Note: If you have a microwave at work, your chances for a good lunch are increased, but let's face it, Pizza is good hot or cold and this one is no exception.

319
CALORIES

MATTERHORN TOSTADA

MENU
- 1 Serving MATTERHORN TOSTADA
- Iced Tea

D E A L - A - M E A L   C A R D S   U S E D

2 BREAD   2 MEAT   1 VEGE   1 FAT

Matterhorn Tostada

- *3 corn tortillas*
- *1 1/2 cups drained, cooked or canned pinto beans*
- *1 clove garlic*
- *1/4 cup sliced red onion*
- *1 tablespoon canned chopped green chile*
- *1/3 cup salsa*
- *1/2 teaspoon cumin*
- *1 1/2 cups shredded lettuce*
- *1 1/4 cups diced tomatoes*
- *3/4 cup steamed sliced carrots, chilled*
- *3 ounces shredded Jack cheese*

1. Preheat oven to 400 degrees. Place tortillas on baking sheet. Bake 5 minutes, or until crisp. Remove from oven. Set aside.
2. In blender, combine beans, garlic, onion, chile, salsa and cumin. Blend.
3. Place tortillas on serving plates. Divide bean mixture over tortillas.
4. Top each serving equally with lettuce, tomatoes, carrots and cheese. Serve with extra salsa, if desired.

Makes 3 servings.

Note: Why the Matterhorn? When we took this photo it reminded us of the Matterhorn at Disneyland. Well doesn't it?

I've tried to lose weight so many times but for all of the wrong reasons. . . for my boyfriend or my mother, or so that I can get a new wardrobe. I've tried and I've failed! Finally for the first time, I'm doing it for myself! I'm doing it because I want to look good and to feel good. I've learned with Deal-A-Meal how to put together healthy foods and enjoy them. In only the first two weeks on Deal-A-Meal I felt better physically and emotionally, thanks to a good diet and excerise.

Juli-anne Davis

Dinner! It's that special time of the day when all the family members join together around the dining room table in a time of fellowship, while chowing down enough food to fill a small grocery store. Then, in a culinary induced stuper, everyone waddles into the den and passes out in front of the TV while watching reruns of *I Love Lucy*. There is no doubt about it, this is America's favorite pastime.

I joke about it, but it's sad. America eats too much food at the dinner hour. I know that at the end of a long, hard day many of us look forward to a nice big dinner. Well, you don't have to be a rocket scientist to know that eating a large fattening meal before you turn in for the night is not going to help you keep your weight under control.

That's why I think this section of recipes is the most important in the entire book. Just take a look at the pictures and then a peek at the calories. You are not going to believe that you will get so much food for so few calories. Not only do these dinners look marvelous, they taste marvelous! And you know, they'll help you look marvelous too!

TABLE OF CONTENTS

354
CALORIES

GLAZED CHICKEN STROGANOFF

MENU
- 1 serving GLAZED CHICKEN STROGANOFF
- 1/3 cup steamed green beans
- Freebie Salad
- 1 tablespoon lo-cal dressing
- Iced Herb Tea

114

1 BREAD   3 MEAT   1 VEGE   1 FAT   1 JOKER

Glazed Chicken Stroganoff

- 1 clove garlic, minced
- 1 shallot, thinly chopped
- 1/4 cup thinly sliced onion
- 1 cup quartered small mushrooms
- 1/4 cup dry white wine
- 1 cup defatted chicken broth
- 6 ounces boned, skinned chicken breast, sliced into thin strips
- 1 tablespoon cornstarch
- Coarsely ground pepper
- 1 teaspoon Worcestershire sauce
- 1 cup cooked drained, wide noodles
- 2 tablespoons sour cream
- Paprika and chopped parsley (optional)

1. In medium skillet, saute' garlic, shallot, onion and mushrooms in white wine, stirring until onions are translucent, about 5 minutes. Add small amount broth as needed, up to 1/4 cup. Remove vegetables and set aside.
2. In same skillet simmer chicken over low heat, in 1/2 cup broth until tender, about 4 minutes.
3. Dissolve cornstarch in remaining 1/4 cup broth and stir into chicken. Stir in seasonings, sour cream and cooked vegetables.
4. Serve over noodles.
5. Sprinkle with paprika and parsley, if desired.

Makes 2 servings.

389
CALORIES

CHICKEN NOODLE CASSEROLE

MENU

- 1 serving CHICKEN NOODLE CASSEROLE
- Freebie Salad
- 2 tablespoons lo-cal dressing
- 1/4 cantaloupe sprinkled with mint sprig and lime slice
- Herb tea

D E A L - A - M E A L C A R D S U S E D

 1 BREAD   2 MEAT   1 VEGE 1 DAIRY   2 FAT   1 FRUIT

Chicken Noodle Casserole

- *2 cups cooked green beans*
- *2 cups cooked drained wide noodles*
- *7 ounces cooked cubed chicken*
- *1/4 cup diet mayonnaise*
- *1 cup low-fat cottage cheese*
- *1/2 teaspoon each salt and lemon pepper seasoning*
- *1/4 teaspoon garlic powder*
- *1/4 cup chopped parsley*
- *3 tablespoons grated Parmesan cheese*

1. Preheat oven to 350 degrees. In 2-quart casserole, layer half of beans, noodles and chicken.
2. Combine mayonnaise, cottage cheese, salt, lemon pepper, garlic powder and parsley. Spread half of mixture over chicken. Sprinkle with half of Parmesan.
3. Repeat layers, ending with cheese.
4. Bake, covered, 30 minutes. Remove cover and bake 15 minutes longer.

Makes 4 servings.

HUNGARIAN GOULASH

MENU
- 1 serving HUNGARIAN GOULASH
- 1/2 cup cooked noodles
- 1/3 cup steamed green beans
- Freebie Salad
- 1 tablespoon lo-cal dressing
- 1/8 cantaloupe with 1/4 cup blueberries
- Herb tea

1 BREAD   4 MEAT   2 VEGE   1 FAT   1 FRUIT

Hungarian Goulash

- *1 pound cubed lean beef*
- *1 cup thinly sliced onion*
- *2 cloves garlic, crushed*
- *1 1/2 tablespoons paprika*
- *2 cups canned tomatoes*
- *1/2 cup (4 ounces) tomato sauce*
- *Coarsely ground pepper*
- *1/2 teaspoon sugar*
- *1/4 cup (4 tablespoons) sour cream*
- *2 cups cooked, drained noodles*
- *Chopped parsley (optional)*

1. In medium non-stick saucepan brown beef on all sides. Remove beef and set aside.
2. In same saucepan saute' onions and garlic stirring until onions are translucent.
3. Return beef to saucepan and add paprika, tomatoes, tomato sauce, pepper and sugar.
4. Cover and simmer over lowest heat 1 hour.
5. Remove cover and simmer 15 minutes longer.
6. Stir in sour cream and serve over noodles.
7. Garnish with parsley, if desired.

Makes 4 servings.

561
CALORIES

TURKEY SCALLOPPINE WITH PASTA PILAF

MENU
- 1 serving TURKEY SCALLOPPINE
- 1 serving PASTA PILAF
- Mixed green salad with 1 cup raw vegetables
- 2 tablespoons lo-cal dressing
- 1/2 cup blackberries
- 1 cup black coffee or tea

120   2 BREAD   4 MEAT   2 VEGE   2 FAT   1 FRUIT   1 JOKER

Turkey Scalloppine

- *5 ounces turkey breast cutlets*
- *3 tablespoons fine dry breadcrumbs*
- *3 tablespoons grated Parmesan cheese*
- *1/2 teaspoon lemon pepper seasoning*
- *1/4 teaspoon dried thyme*
- *1 teaspoon olive oil*
- *1 teaspoon butter or margarine*
- *1/2 cup prepared all-natural spaghetti sauce*
- *2 ounces shredded mozzarella cheese*

1. Place cutlets between layers of waxed paper and pound until flattened.
2. In shallow dish, combine breadcrumbs, Parmesan and seasonings.
3. Lightly moisten cutlets with a little water, then coat with crumb mixture.
4. Place in refrigerator 30 minutes to allow coating to set.
5. Preheat broiler. In medium non-stick skillet, heat oil and butter. Add cutlets and brown on both sides over medium-high heat.
6. Turn heat to low and continue to cook just until cutlets are done, about 3 minutes.
7. Top with spaghetti sauce and cheese.
8. Place under broiler about 1 minute or until cheese is hot and bubbly.

Makes 2 servings.

INGREDIENTS   **DIRECTIONS**

Pasta Pilaf

- *1/2 cup uncooked broken spaghetti*
- *1/4 cup uncooked rice*
- *1 1/3 cups defatted chicken broth, heated*
- *1 strip lemon zest minced (optional)*
- *1 tablespoon chopped parsley (optional)*

1. In medium non-stick skillet, coated with non-stick spray, brown spaghetti over medium heat stirring constantly to prevent burning.
2. Add rice and hot broth. Stir, then cover tightly. Turn heat to low and cook 20 minutes without lifting cover.
3. Remove cover and continue to cook until all liquid has evaporated. Stir in lemon zest and parsley, if desired.

Makes 2 servings.

407
CALORIES

TURKEY SCHNITZEL WITH MUSHROOMS WITH SNOWY POTATOES

MENU

- 1 serving TURKEY SCHNITZEL WITH MUSHROOMS
- 1 serving SNOWY POTATOES
- Asparagus Spears
- 1 small apple
- 1 cup black coffee or tea

122   2 BREAD   3 MEAT   1 VEGE   1 FAT 1 FRUIT   1 JOKER

Turkey Schnitzel With Mushrooms

- *5 ounces turkey breast cutlets*
- *3 tablespoons fine, dry breadcrumbs*
- *1/4 teaspoon lemon pepper seasoning*
- *1/8 teaspoon each dried rosemary and thyme*
- *1/2 teaspoon each butter or margarine and olive oil*
- *1 cup sliced mushrooms*
- *3/4 cup defatted chicken broth*
- *1 tablespoon cornstarch*
- *1/4 teaspoon garlic powder*
- *Salt and pepper to taste*
- *1 ounce shredded mozzarella cheese*

1. Place cutlets between layers of wax paper and pound with a rolling pin or side of a bottle until flattened.
2. In shallow dish combine breadcrumbs and seasonings.
3. Lightly moisten cutlets with water, then coat with crumb mixture. Place in refrigerator for 30 minutes to allow coating to set.
4. Preheat broiler. Meanwhile, in medium saucepan, saute' mushrooms and garlic powder in 1/4 cup of broth.
5. Dissolve cornstarch in 2 tablespoons broth and add to mushrooms with remaining broth. Stir until sauce boils and thickens. Add salt and pepper to taste. Keep warm.
6. In medium non-stick skillet, coated with non-stick spray, quickly brown cutlets on both sides over medium-high heat.
7. Turn heat to low and continue to cook just until cutlets are done, about 3 minutes.
8. Sprinkle cheese over cutlets and place under broiler about 1 minute or until cheese is hot and bubbly.
9. To serve, pour mushroom sauce over turkey.

Makes 2 servings.

INGREDIENTS   DIRECTIONS

Snowy Potatoes

- *3 small peeled, cubed potatoes*
- *2 teaspoons butter or margarine*
- *1/4 cup hot non-fat milk*
- *Salt and pepper to taste*

1. In medium saucepan, boil potatoes in water to cover. When tender, drain.
2. Return pan to stove and shake over medium heat to evaporate some of moisture.
3. Mash potatoes thoroughly. Add butter and hot milk and continue to mash until blended. Season to taste. Beat potatoes with wooden spoon until very light and fluffy.

Makes 2 servings.

POLLO PARMESANO

MENU

- 1 serving POLLO PARMESANO
- 1 cup mixed steamed broccoli and carrots
- Freebie Salad
- 2 tablespoons lo-cal dressing
- 1 breadstick
- 1 cup fruit-flavored gelatin with 1/2 banana, sliced
- Iced herb tea

D E A L - A - M E A L   C A R D S   U S E D

 1 BREAD   2 MEAT   2 VEGE   1 FAT 1 FRUIT   1 JOKER

Pollo Parmesano

- *6 tablespoons fine dry bread crumbs*
- *3 tablespoons grated Parmesan cheese*
- *1 tablespoon chopped parsley*
- *1/4 teaspoon each garlic powder and paprika*
- *1/8 teaspoon each thyme and sage*
- *Coarsely ground pepper*
- *4 small chicken thighs skinned*
- *1/3 cup chicken broth*
- *1/4 cup sherry or chicken broth*

1. Preheat oven to 350 degrees.
2. In plastic bag, combine breadcrumbs, Parmesan, parsley and seasonings.
3. Place chicken pieces in bag, one at a time and shake bag to coat chicken.
4. Arrange coated chicken in single layer in small, shallow roasting dish. Pour broth into dish.
5. Bake, uncovered, 30 minutes, basting occasionally.
6. Pour sherry or additional broth over chicken. Cover and bake 10 minutes longer.
7. Remove cover. Baste chicken and bake 5 minutes longer.

Makes 4 servings.

270
CALORIES

GREEK GRILLED LAMB CHOPS

MENU
- 1 serving GREEK GRILLED LAMB CHOPS
- 1 small ear of corn
- Half broiled tomato
- 1/2 cup steamed green beans
- 1 small pear
- Mineral water

D E A L - A - M E A L   C A R D S   U S E D

 1 BREAD 2 MEAT 2 VEGE 1 FAT 1 FRUIT

Greek Grilled Lamb Chops

- 4 small lamb chops, trimmed of fat
- 4 teaspoons olive oil
- 2 tablespoons lemon juice
- 1 teaspoon low-sodium soy sauce
- 1/4 teaspoon coarsely ground pepper
- 1/2 teaspoon _each_ dried oregano and dried rosemary
- 1 large clove garlic, finely chopped
- 1 bay leaf

1. Place chops in sealable plastic bag.
2. In small bowl combine remaining ingredients and pour over chops. Press out as much air as possible and then seal bag.
3. Marinate at least 4 hours in refrigerator.
4. Lift chops from marinade and broil or barbecue, brushing with marinade occasionally, about 4 to 6 minutes on each side, or until done as desired.

Makes 4 servings.

264
CALORIES

TURKEY PUMPKIN PIE

MENU

- 1 serving TURKEY PUMPKIN PIE
- 3 steamed asparagus spears
- Freebie Salad
- 2 tablespoons lo-cal dressing
- 12 grapes
- 1 cup black coffee

D E A L - A - M E A L   C A R D S   U S E D

 1 BREAD   2 MEAT   1 VEGE   1 FAT   1 FRUIT

Turkey Pumpkin Pie

- *1 cup chopped onion*
- *1 cup chopped cabbage*
- *7 ounces ground turkey*
- *1 cup cooked brown rice*
- *1/2 cup tomato sauce*
- *1/4 teaspoon <u>each</u> sage, thyme, basil and oregano*
- *Salt and pepper to taste*
- *1 1/2 cups cooked, mashed pumpkin*
- *3 tablespoons grated Parmesan cheese*
- *1/4 cup chopped parsley*
- *1/4 teaspoon nutmeg*

1. Preheat oven to 375 degrees.
2. In skillet, saute' onion and cabbage with turkey, until onion is translucent and meat is browned and crumbly. Drain excess fat.
3. Stir in cooked rice, tomato sauce, sage, thyme, basil and oregano. Season with salt and pepper to taste.
4. Press mixture into bottom of 9-inch square baking dish.
5. In medium bowl, combine pumpkin, 2 tablespoons of Parmesan, parsley and nutmeg. Season with salt and pepper to taste.
6. Spread over turkey mixture. Sprinkle with remaining tablespoon of Parmesan.
7. Bake 20 minutes or until heated through and lightly browned on top.

Makes 4 servings.

262
CALORIES

TURKEY VEGETABLE HARVEST

MENU
- 1 serving TURKEY VEGETABLE HARVEST
- Freebie Salad
- 2 tablespoons lo-cal dressing
- 1 breadstick
- 1 small apple
- 1 cup black coffee or tea

130   1 BREAD   2 MEAT   1 VEGE   1 DAIRY   2 FAT   1 FRUIT

Turkey Vegetable Harvest

- *1 pound ground turkey*
- *3/4 cup each diced onion and sliced celery*
- *1/2 cup chopped green pepper*
- *1/2 teaspoon each nutmeg, garlic powder and curry powder*
- *1/4 teaspoon pepper*
- *2 cups sliced summer squash*
- *1 cup shredded cabbage*
- *1 cup sliced mushrooms*
- *2 cups tomato wedges*
- *2 cups cooked rice*
- *1 tablespoon red wine vinegar*
- *1 tablespoon Worcestershire sauce*

1. In large, heavy skillet, saute' turkey with onion, celery and green pepper, stirring until turkey is brown and crumbly. Drain excess fat.
2. Stir in seasonings. Add squash, cabbage and mushrooms.
3. Cover and simmer until vegetables are tender.
4. Stir in tomatoes and rice. Heat through.
5. Stir in vinegar and Worcestershire.

Makes 8 servings.

325
CALORIES

TEXAS TURKEY CHILI

MENU
- 1 serving TEXAS TURKEY CHILI
- 1 corn tortilla
- Freebie Salad
- 2 tablespoons lo-cal dressing
- 1/2 papaya with lime wedge
- 1 cup black coffee or tea

DEAL - A - MEAL CARDS USED

132   2 BREAD   3 MEAT   1 VEGE   1 FAT   1 FRUIT

Texas Turkey Chili
- *1 pound ground turkey*
- *1 cup thinly sliced onion*
- *1 large clove garlic, crushed*
- *1 tablespoon chili powder*
- *1 (16-ounce) can Mexican-style tomatoes, undrained*
- *1 cup drained, canned pinto beans or kidney beans*
- *1 1/3 cups frozen whole kernel corn*

1. In large skillet, saute' turkey, onion, garlic and chili powder, stirring until turkey is crumbled and no longer pink. Drain excess fat.
2. Stir in remaining ingredients. Bring to boil.
3. Cover and simmer 10 to 15 minutes.

Makes 6 servings.

Variation: Tofu Chili
- *1 cup thinly sliced onion*
- *1 large clove garlic, crushed*
- *1 tablespoon chili powder*
- *1/2 cup defatted chicken broth*
- *1 (16-ounce) can Mexican-style tomatoes, undrained*
- *1 cup drained, canned pinto beans or kidney beans*
- *1 1/3 cups frozen whole kernel corn*
- *2 cups drained, cubed firm tofu*
- *2 ounces low-fat mozzarella cheese*

1. In large skillet, saute' onion and garlic with chili powder, in broth about 5 minutes.
2. Stir in remaining ingredients except cheese. Bring to boil.
3. Cover and simmer 10 minutes. To serve, sprinkle with cheese.

Makes 6 servings.

Note: Count 1 meat card instead of three. Remainder of menu is the same. Tofu Chili menu equals 328 calories.

498
CALORIES

HURRY CURRY

MENU

- 1 serving HURRY CURRY
- 1 cup fruit-flavored diet gelatin set with 1/2 cup fruit cocktail
- 1 cup black coffee or tea

D E A L - A - M E A L   C A R D S   U S E D

134   1 BREAD   2 MEAT   1 VEGE

Hurry Curry

- 2 cloves garlic, crushed
- 1 cup chopped onion
- 1/2 cup <u>each</u> sliced celery and chopped green pepper
- 1 pound lean ground beef
- 1 1/2 to 2 tablespoons curry powder
- 1 cup tomato sauce
- 2 tablespoons Worcestershire sauce
- 1 cup defatted chicken broth
- 1 cup cubed, unpeeled eggplant
- 1 cup sliced carrots
- 1 small unpeeled potato, cubed
- 1/2 cup peeled, cubed winter squash
- 1 cup sliced mushrooms
- 1 cup frozen peas
- 3 cups cooked rice

1. In large skillet, saute' garlic, onion, celery, green pepper and beef until onion is translucent and beef is browned. Drain excess fat.
2. Stir in curry powder and cook 2 minutes.
3. Add tomato sauce, Worcestershire, broth, eggplant, carrots, potato and squash.
4. Cover and simmer over low heat until vegetables are almost tender.
5. Add mushrooms and peas. Cook 5 minutes longer.
6. Stir in rice. Heat thoroughly.

Makes 8 servings.

TIERED TURKEY TERRINE

MENU
- 1 serving TIERED TURKEY TERRINE
- Freebie Salad
- 2 tablespoons lo-cal dressing
- 1/2 cup strawberries and 2 tablespoons blueberries
- Iced herb tea

D E A L - A - M E A L   C A R D S   U S E D

136   1 BREAD   3 MEAT   1 VEGE   1 FAT   1 FRUIT

Tiered Turkey Terrine

- 1 pound ground turkey
- 1 slice wholewheat bread, crumbed
- 6 tablespoons uncooked oatmeal
- 1/2 cup chopped onion
- 1/4 cup chopped celery
- 2 tablespoons chopped parsley
- 1/2 cup tomato sauce
- 1 tablespoon each low- sodium soy sauce and Worcestershire sauce
- 1/2 teaspoon garlic powder
- 1/4 teaspoon dried dill weed
- 2 egg whites
- 2 cups thinly shredded spinach (steamed briefly and drained)
- 3/4 cup chopped fresh mushrooms
- 1/2 cup grated carrots
- 1/4 teaspoon nutmeg
- 2 ounces shredded low-fat Cheddar cheese

1. Preheat oven to 350 degrees. In large bowl, mix turkey with bread, oatmeal, onion, celery, parsley, tomato sauce, soy sauce, Worcestershire, garlic powder, dill and egg whites. Mix thoroughly.
2. Place 1/3 of mixture in 9x5-inch loaf pan, coated with non-stick spray.
3. Cover with half of spinach, then mushrooms and carrots. Sprinkle with 1/8 teaspoon nutmeg and half of cheese.
4. Cover with another 1/3 of meat loaf mixture, then layer remaining spinach, mushrooms and carrot on top. Sprinkle with remaining nutmeg and cheese.
5. Cover with last 1/3 of meat loaf mixture. Bake 1 hour.
6. Let stand 15 minutes,then invert onto heated serving plate and slice to serve.

Makes 6 servings.

281

CALORIES

ORANGE ROUGHY IN A STEAMBATH

MENU

- ORANGE ROUGHY IN A STEAMBATH
- 3 steamed baby red potatoes or
  1 small steamed red potato, cut up
- 1/3 cup steamed, sliced summer squash
- Mixed green salad with 1 cup raw vegetables,
  such as sliced mushrooms and cherry tomatoes
- 2 tablespoons lo-cal dressing
- 1 small apple
- 1 cup black coffee or tea

D E A L · A · M E A L   C A R D S   U S E D

 1 BREAD   2 MEAT   2 VEGE   1 FAT

Orange Roughy in a Steambath

- *1 onion slice, separated into rings*
- *2 ounces Orange Roughy or other white fish*
- *2 slices lime*
- *3 to 4 capers*
- *1/4 cup chicken or vegetable broth*

1. Scatter onion rings over bottom of small skillet. Place fish on top of onion.
2. Arrange lime slices over fish and sprinkle with capers. Pour in broth.
3. Cover skillet and steam gently 5 minutes, or until fish flakes easily with fork.

Makes 1 serving.

480
CALORIES

FISH FLORENTINE WITH POTATOES ANNA

MENU
- 1 serving FISH FLORENTINE
- 1 serving POTATOES ANNA
- 2/3 cup steamed mixed carrots and peas
- 1/2 cup blueberries with
- 3/4 cup plain non-fat yogurt
- 1 cup black coffee or tea

D E A L · A · M E A L   C A R D S   U S E D

140

1 BREAD 2 MEAT 2 VEGE 1 DAIRY 2 FAT 1 FRUIT

Fish Florentine

- *1 cup cooked, drained chopped spinach*
- *1 tablespoon instant minced onion*
- *1/4 teaspoon each garlic powder and nutmeg*
- *Dash salt and pepper*
- *1/4 cup (4 tablespoons) sour cream*
- *7 ounces any firm-fleshed fish, such as Red Snapper, Halibut, Cod*
- *3 tablespoons grated Parmesan cheese*
- *2 tablespoons chopped parsley*
- *1/2 teaspoon Italian mixed herbs*
- *8 slices tomato*

1. Preheat oven to 400 degrees. Mix spinach with onion, garlic powder, nutmeg, salt, pepper and sour cream.
2. Spread spinach mixture over bottom of small shallow baking dish.
3. Arrange fish over spinach.
4. Cover with tomato slices.
5. Combine Parmesan, parsley and herbs. Sprinkle mixture over tomatoes and fish.
6. Bake 15 minutes, or until fish flakes when tested with fork.

Makes 4 servings.

INGREDIENTS   DIRECTIONS

Potatoes Anna

- *2 small baking potatoes, peeled and thinly sliced*
- *2 tablespoons each chopped green onion and parsley*
- *Salt and pepper to taste*
- *4 teaspoons butter or margarine, melted*
- *1/2 cup evaporated skim milk*

1. Preheat oven to 350 degrees. Coat 10-inch pie plate with non-stick spray.
2. In pie plate, arrange potato slices in overlapping layers, sprinkling slices with onion and parsley.
3. Season with salt and pepper to taste.
4. Pour butter over potatoes.
5. Pour milk over all. Cover. Bake 45 minutes.
6. Remove cover and bake 15 to 20 minutes longer until potatoes are tender and golden brown.

Makes 4 servings.

273
CALORIES

HAPPY COAT FISH FILLETS WITH GINGERED CUCUMBERS
MENU
- 1 serving HAPPY COAT FISH FILLETS
- GINGERED CUCUMBERS
- 1/2 cup steamed rice
- 1 cup steamed pea pods and mushrooms
- 1/3 cup Mandarin orange sections
- 1 cup tea

D E A L - A - M E A L   C A R D S   U S E D

  1 BREAD   2 MEAT   2 VEGE   1 FRUIT

Happy Coat Fish Fillets

- *8 ounces any firm-fleshed fish such as Red Snapper, Orange Roughy, Halibut, Cod*
- *Lemon juice*
- *1/2 teaspoon grated fresh ginger root*
- *2 tablespoons thinly sliced green onion*
- *1 cup defatted chicken broth*
- *1 tablespoon cornstarch*
- *2 teaspoons low-sodium soy sauce*
- *2 tablespoons sherry*

1. Preheat broiler. Sprinkle fish with lemon juice and broil 4 to 6 inches from heat, about 4 minutes per side, or until fish flakes when tested with fork.
2. Meanwhile, in small saucepan, saute' ginger and green onion in small amount of broth until onion is tender, about 4 minutes.
3. Stir cornstarch into soy sauce until dissolved and add to saucepan with sherry and remaining broth.
4. Stir until sauce boils and thickens. Pour over fish.

Makes 4 servings.

Gingered Cucumbers

- *1 European cucumber*
- *1 teaspoon salt*
- *1/4 cup rice vinegar*
- *1 tablespoon sugar*
- *1 teaspoon grated fresh ginger root*

1. Peel cucumber and score with fork. Cut into thin slices.
2. In shallow dish, sprinkle cucumber slices with salt and let stand 30 minutes.
3. Drain liquid. Combine remaining ingredients. Pour over cucumber. Mix well.
4. Refrigerate several hours before serving.

Makes 4 servings.

344
CALORIES

SPICY SWEET 'N SOUR CHICKEN
WITH RICE AND VEGE MEDLEY
MENU
- 1 serving SPICY SWEET 'N SOUR CHICKEN
- 1 serving RICE AND VEGE MEDLEY
- 1/2 cup pineapple chunks
- 1 cup tea

D E A L - A - M E A L   C A R D S   U S E D

144   1 BREAD   3 MEAT   1 VEGE   1 FAT   1 FRUIT

INGREDIENTS

Spicy Sweet 'N Sour Chicken
- 1/3 cup unsweetened apple juice
- 2 dried apricots, diced
- 1 clove garlic, finely chopped
- 2 slices onion
- 1 bay leaf
- 1 tablespoon white wine vinegar
- 1/2 teaspoon grated fresh ginger root
- 1/8 teaspoon coarsely ground pepper
- 12 ounces boned, skinned chicken breast

DIRECTIONS

1. In sealable plastic bag, combine all ingredients. Seal. Allow chicken to marinate several hours in refrigerator.
2. Preheat oven to 350 degrees. Transfer chicken with marinade to baking dish.
3. Bake, uncovered, 35 minutes. Lift chicken out and discard marinade.

Makes 4 servings.

INGREDIENTS

Rice and Vege Medley
- 4 teaspoons dark, sesame oil
- 4 cups mixed chopped vegetables, such as carrots, zucchini, broccoli, mushrooms, green onion
- 2 cups cooked brown rice

DIRECTIONS

1. In large non-stick skillet, heat sesame oil. Add vegetables and quickly saute until tender crisp.
2. Add cooked rice. Stir until rice is hot.

Makes 4 servings.

FISH MEDITERRANEAN

MENU

- FISH MEDITERRANEAN
- Freebie Salad with
- 2 tablespoons lo-cal dressing
- 1 kiwifruit
- 1 cup black coffee or tea

1 BREAD   2 MEAT   2 VEGE   2 FAT   1 FRUIT

INGREDIENTS

DIRECTIONS

Fish Mediterranean

- 1/4 cup _each_ chopped onion and parsley
- 1 clove garlic, crushed
- 1 teaspoon olive oil
- 3/4 cup canned chopped tomatoes
- 1/4 cup red wine
- 1/4 teaspoon dried basil
- 1/8 teaspoon dried oregano
- 2 ounces fish, such as Halibut, Red Snapper or Cod, cubed.
- Salt and pepper to taste
- 1/2 cup cooked, drained linguine noodles

1. In medium saucepan saute' onion, parsley and garlic in olive oil.
2. Add tomatoes, wine, basil and oregano. Cover and simmer 10 minutes.
3. Add fish, cover and simmer 5 minutes or until fish flakes when tested with fork.
4. Season with salt and pepper to taste.
5. Serve in bowl over linguine.

Makes 1 serving.

348

CALORIES

IT AIN'T MEAT LASAGNE

MENU

- Wine Spritzer with 2 ounces red wine
- 1 serving IT AIN'T MEAT LASAGNE
- Freebie Salad
- 1 tablespoon lo-cal dressing
- 1 serving crusty bread
- 1/2 medium peach and 1/4 cup raspberries

D E A L - A - M E A L   C A R D S   U S E D

150   2 BREAD   1 MEAT   1 VEGE   2 FAT   1 FRUIT

It Ain't Meat Lasagne

- 2 (10-ounce) packages frozen chopped broccoli
- 1 cup drained, soft tofu
- 1/4 cup lemon juice
- 1 teaspoon dried oregano
- 1/2 teaspoon _each_ garlic powder and nutmeg
- 2 teaspoons sugar
- Italian Sauce (recipe follows)
- 8 lasagne noodles, cooked and drained
- 1 1/2 cups (6 ounces) shredded low-fat mozzarella cheese
- 6 tablespoons grated Parmesan cheese

1. Preheat oven to 350 degrees. Cook broccoli according to package directions. Drain.
2. In blender or food processor, combine tofu, lemon juice, oregano, garlic powder, nutmeg and sugar. Stir in broccoli.
3. Cover bottom of 9x13-inch baking pan with thin layer of Italian Sauce.
4. Arrange 4 lasagne noodles over sauce.
5. Spread half of broccoli tofu mixture over noodles.
6. Sprinkle with half of mozzarella.
7. Make one more layer using half of remaining sauce, remaining 4 noodles and remaining broccoli tofu mixture.
8. Sprinkle with remaining mozzarella.
9. Cover with remaining sauce and sprinkle Parmesan over top.
10. Bake 30 minutes. Let stand 10 minutes.

Makes 10 servings.

INGREDIENTS DIRECTIONS

Italian Sauce

- 5 teaspoons olive oil
- 2 cloves garlic, crushed
- 1 cup grated carrots
- 1 (28-ounce) can tomato puree
- 1/4 cup chopped parsley
- 1 tablespoon lemon juice
- 1/2 teaspoon sugar
- 1 teaspoon _each_ dried basil and oregano

1. In large saucepan, heat olive oil. Add garlic and carrots and saute' until garlic just starts to brown.
2. Add remaining ingredients. Cover and simmer over low heat 15 minutes.

Makes about 4 cups sauce.

369
CALORIES

SPAGHETTI AND CHICKEN BALL PIE

MENU
- 1 juice spritzer
- 1 serving SPAGHETTI AND CHICKEN BALL PIE
- Freebie Salad
- 2 tablespoons lo-cal dressing
- 2 plums
- 1 cup black coffee or tea

D E A L - A - M E A L   C A R D S   U S E D

154 1 BREAD 2 MEAT 1 VEGE 2 FAT 1 FRUIT 1 JOKER

Spaghetti and Chicken Ball Pie

Crust:
- 2 cups cooked, drained spaghetti
- 1 egg, lightly beaten
- 1/4 cup chopped parsley
- 1 tablespoon grated Parmesan cheese
- 1/4 teaspoon dried oregano
- 1/8 teaspoon coarsely ground pepper

Chicken Balls:
- 6 tablespoons fine dry breadcrumbs
- 1/4 cup chopped parsley
- 2 tablespoons *each* finely chopped shallots and mushrooms
- 1/4 teaspoon *each* dried thyme, basil, oregano and paprika
- 1/8 teaspoon *each* salt and pepper
- 6 ounces lean ground chicken 1 egg, lightly beaten

Filling;
- 3/4 cup prepared all-natural spaghetti sauce
- 2 teaspoons olive oil
- 1 clove garlic, crushed
- 1/4 cup *each* chopped red and green pepper
- 3/4 cup *each* thinly sliced Japanese eggplant, zucchini and mushrooms
- 1/8 teaspoon dried oregano
- Dash pepper
- 3 ounces shredded Jack cheese
- 2 tablespoons grated Parmesan cheese

1. Preheat oven to 425 degrees.
2. For crust, in medium bowl, combine all ingredients.
3. Turn into 9-inch pie plate coated with non-stick spray. Arrange spaghetti over bottom and sides of pie plate.
4. Bake 5 minutes. Remove from oven and reduce oven temperature to 350 degrees.
5. For chicken balls, in medium bowl, combine all ingredients. Shape into 12 balls.
6. To fill pie, first spread a thin layer of spaghetti sauce, about 3 tablespoons, over crust. Arrange balls around outer edge of crust to form a circle.
7. In medium non-stick skillet, heat olive oil and saute garlic, red and green pepper, eggplant, zucchini and mushrooms over high heat, stirring constantly about 5 minutes. Sprinkle with oregano and pepper.
8. Place half of vegetables in center of pie crust. Sprinkle with a little Jack cheese and add remaining vegetables.
9. Cover chicken balls and vegetables with remaining spaghetti sauce. Sprinkle with remaining Jack cheese and Parmesan.
10. Bake 20 minutes. Let sit about 5 minutes before slicing.

Makes 6 servings.

301
CALORIES

PASTA PRIMAVERA

MENU
- 1 serving PASTA PRIMAVERA
- Freebie Salad
- 2 tablespoons lo-cal dressing
- 3/4 cup fresh strawberries
- 1 cup black coffee or tea

DEAL - A - MEAL CARDS USED

  1 BREAD 1 MEAT 1 VEGE 2 FAT

Pasta Primavera

- 4 teaspoons olive oil
- 1 clove garlic, crushed
- 1/2 cup chopped onion
- 1 cup sliced zucchini
- 3/4 cup sliced mushrooms
- 1 cup broccoli flowerettes
- 1/4 cup chicken broth or water
- 3/4 cup halved cherry tomatoes
- 1/4 cup chopped parsley
- 1 teaspoon lemon juice
- 1 teaspoon dried basil
- 1/2 teaspoon dried oregano
- Coarsely ground pepper
- 2 cups cooked, drained
  spaghetti
- 2 ounces shredded mozzarella
  cheese
- 6 tablespoons grated Parmesan
  cheese

1. In large skillet, heat olive oil. Add garlic, onion, zucchini and mushrooms and saute' until onion is translucent.
2. Add broccoli and broth. Cover and steam 5 to 7 minutes or until broccoli is just tender crisp.
3. Add tomatoes, parsley, lemon juice and seasonings. Toss thoroughly.
4. Serve over spaghetti. Sprinkle with mozzarella and Parmesan .

Makes 4 servings.

386
CALORIES

ENCHILADA SUIZA WITH MEXICAN RICE

MENU
- 1 juice spritzer
- 1 serving ENCHILADA SUIZA
- 1 serving MEXICAN RICE
- 1/2 cup steamed green beans
- 1/2 cup fresh pineapple cubes

D E A L - A - M E A L   C A R D S   U S E D

158   2 BREAD   2 MEAT   2 VEGE   1 FRUIT   2 JOKER

| INGREDIENTS | DIRECTIONS |

Enchilada Suiza
- *6 corn tortillas*
- *Suiza Sauce (recipe follows)*
- *12 ounces poached chicken*
- *1 cup chopped green onion*

1. Preheat oven to 350 degrees. Steam tortillas or warm in microwave until soft.
2. For each enchilada, dip 1 tortilla into Suiza Sauce. Place 2 ounces chicken down center of tortilla. Roll up and place seam side down in 9x13-inch baking dish.
3. Pour remaining sauce over enchiladas and cover dish.
4. Bake 15 to 20 minutes or until heated through.
5. Serve sprinkled with green onion.

Makes 6 servings.

| INGREDIENTS | DIRECTIONS |

Suiza Sauce
- *1 clove garlic, crushed*
- *1 cup finely chopped onion*
- *1 tablespoon chili powder*
- *1 teaspoon ground cumin*
- *1/4 cup chicken broth or water*
- *1 cup tomato puree*
- *1 cup evaporated skim milk*
- *1 cup low-fat cottage cheese*

1. In medium non-stick skillet, saute' garlic, onion, chili powder and cumin in broth until onion is translucent.
2. Stir in tomato puree'. Bring to boil. Reduce heat and simmer 15 minutes or until sauce is thick.
3. Slowly stir in milk, then cottage cheese. Heat gently. Do not boil.

| INGREDIENTS | DIRECTIONS |

Mexican Rice
- *1/2 cup chopped onion*
- *1 cup rice*
- *1 teaspoon chili powder*
- *2 cups defatted chicken broth*
- *1/2 cup tomato sauce*
- *Coarsely ground pepper*
- *2 teaspoons chopped cilantro (optional)*

1. In medium non-stick saucepan, saute' onion and rice in small amount of broth until onion is translucent.
2. Add chili powder and mix well.
3. Stir in tomato sauce, remaining broth and pepper.
4. Bring to boil. Cover and reduce heat. Simmer 20 minutes or until all liquid is absorbed.
5. Stir in cilantro, if desired.

Makes 6 servings.

384
CALORIES

THIS CHICK WAS MADE FOR WOKING

MENU
- 1 serving THIS CHICK WAS MADE FOR WOKING
- 1/2 cup mixed Mandarin orange segments and pineapple chunks
- 1 cup hot tea

D E A L - A - M E A L   C A R D S   U S E D

160   1 BREAD   3 MEAT   1 VEGE   1 FAT

This Chick Was
Made for Woking

- *3 cloves garlic, crushed*
- *2 teaspoons grated fresh ginger root*
- *1/4 cup dry sherry*
- *1 tablespoon low-sodium soy sauce*
- *2 teaspoons dark sesame oil*
- *12 ounces boned skinned chicken, cubed.*
- *1/2 cup defatted chicken broth*
- *4 cups mixed raw vegetables such as sliced onions, sliced celery, green pepper strips, Chinese pea pods, bean sprouts and sliced mushrooms*
- *2 teaspoons cornstarch dissolved in 1 tablespoon cold water*
- *2 cups cooked rice*
- *12 almonds, sliced and toasted*

1. In glass bowl, combine garlic, ginger root, sherry, soy sauce and sesame oil. Stir in chicken and marinate, covered, in refrigerator at least 1 hour. Stir occasionally.
2. In large wok or skillet, bring broth to boil.
3. Add onions, celery and green pepper. Cook and stir about 2 minutes. Add pea pods and cook 1 minute more, then add bean sprouts and mushrooms and cook 2 more minutes. Vegetables should still be tender crisp.
4. Remove vegetables from skillet onto heated plate . Keep warm.
5. Add chicken with marinade to wok and cook, stirring over high heat 4 minutes, or until chicken is opaque. Return vegetables to skillet and stir to heat through.
6. Using slotted spoon, lift chicken and vegetables from wok onto plate of hot rice.
7. Stir dissolved cornstarch into liquid in wok and heat stirring constantly until thickened. Pour over chicken and rice.
8. Serve, sprinkled with almonds.

Makes 4 servings.

329
CALORIES

MOUSSAKA

MENU
- 1 serving MOUSSAKA
- Freebie Salad
- 2 tablespoons lo-cal dressing
- 12 grapes
- 1 cup black coffee or tea

162   3 MEAT   1 VEGE   2 FAT   1 FRUIT

Moussaka

- 1 cup finely chopped onion
- 1 1/2 pounds lean ground beef or lamb
- 1/2 teaspoon garlic powder
- 1 teaspoon dried basil
- 1/2 teaspoon _each_ dried oregano, cinnamon and seasoned salt
- Dash pepper
- 2 (8-ounce) cans tomato sauce
- 2 small eggplants
- 2 tablespoons butter or margarine
- 2 tablespoons all-purpose flour
- 1/4 teaspoon salt
- 2 cups low-fat milk
- 2 eggs
- 6 tablespoons grated Parmesan cheese
- 1/2 cup (2 ounces) shredded Cheddar cheese

1. Preheat oven to 350 degrees. In large non-stick skillet, saute' onion, beef and garlic powder. When meat is browned and crumbly, drain excess fat.
2. Add basil, oregano, cinnamon, seasoned salt, pepper and tomato sauce. Bring to boil then reduce heat and simmer, uncovered 20 minutes.
3. Meanwhile, halve unpeeled eggplants lengthwise. Slice crosswise into 1/2 inch thick slices. Steam about 10 minutes or microwave about 6 minutes or until tender. Set aside.
4. In medium saucepan, melt butter. Stir in flour and salt. Add milk gradually, stirring over low heat, until mixture comes to boil and thickens. Remove from heat.
5. In small bowl, whisk eggs. Whisk in 1/4 cup sauce. Pour egg mixture back into saucepan and whisk to blend thoroughly. Set aside.
6. In 9x13-inch baking dish, layer half of eggplant slices, overlapping slightly.
7. Sprinkle with 2 tablespoons _each_ Parmesan and Cheddar, then spoon meat sauce evenly over top.
8. Sprinkle with another 2 tablespoons of each cheese.
9. Layer remaining eggplant over top. Pour sauce over all. Sprinkle with remaining cheese.
10. Bake 40 minutes or until golden brown and sauce is set. Let stand about 10 minutes before cutting into squares.

Makes 10 servings.